VOL **4** CEL-COL
263–350

FUNK & WAGNALLS **new**
ENCYCLOPEDIA
OF SCIENCE

FUNK & WAGNALLS, INC.

HOW TO USE FUNK & WAGNALLS NEW ENCYCLOPEDIA OF SCIENCE

Volumes 1 through 21 have information printed on the front covers, spine, and title pages that make it easy to find the articles you want to read.

- Volume numbers are printed in all three places in Volumes 1 through 21.
- Letter breaks — $\frac{COL}{DIA}$ — are printed in all three places in Volumes 1 through 21. The letters above the line are the first three letters of the first article title in the volume. The letters below the line are the first three letters of the last article title in the volume.
- Page breaks — $\frac{351}{438}$ — are printed on the spines and title pages of Volumes 1 through 21. They provide the page numbers of the first and last text pages in the volume.

Articles are arranged alphabetically by title in Volumes 1 through 21. Most titles are printed in **BOLD-FACE CAPITAL** letters. Some titles are printed in even larger letters.

- Some titles are not article titles, but refer you to the actual article title. Within articles you will find *See* or *See also* other article names for further information. All of these references to other articles are called cross-references.
- Most article titles are followed by a phonetic pronunciation. Use the Pronunciation Guide on page vi of Volume 1 to learn the correct pronunciation of the article title.
- At the end of most articles are two sets of initials. The first set identifies the person who wrote the article. The second set identifies the special consultant who checked the article for accuracy. All of these people are listed by their initials and full names and position on pages v and vi of Volume 1.
- ◤ This symbol at the end of an article indicates that there is a project based on the subject of the article in the Projects, Bibliography & Index volume. The project is found under its article title, and all of the project article titles are arranged alphabetically on pages 1 through 64 of the Projects, Bibliography & Index volume.

The Projects, Bibliography & Index Volume contains three sections. Each is an essential part of the encyclopedia.

- Projects based on articles in the encyclopedia are found in the first section. Each is both entertaining and educational. Each is designed for use by a student and for parental participation if desired.
- Bibliography reading lists in the second section list books under general scientific categories that are also titles of major articles. Each book listed is marked with either a YA (Young Adult) or J (Juvenile) reading level indicator. YA generally applies to readers at the junior high level or higher. J applies to readers at grade levels below junior high school.
- Index entries for all article titles plus many subjects that are not article titles are found in the third section. Instructions on using the Index are found at the start of the Index section in the Projects, Bibliography & Index volume.

CAVITATION (kav′ə tā′ shən) Cavitation is the formation of bubbles or cavities (hollow places) behind a body that is moving rapidly in a liquid. For example, cavitation occurs behind the blade of a boat's propeller when the boat is moving. As a boat moves through water, the propeller pushes against the water. This thrusts the boat forward. If cavitation occurs, the propeller spins in a pocket of air and does not work the way it was designed to. Cavitation also absorbs a great deal of energy, reducing a propeller's efficiency. Proper design can prevent cavitation from occuring.

J.J.A./R.W.L.

CEDAR (sēd′ ər) A cedar is a coniferous tree that belongs to the Pinaceae family. (*See* CON-IFER.) There are many species of cedars which belong to different groups. True cedars are large trees found in Europe and Asia. The cedar of Lebanon grows in the Middle East nation of Lebanon. In North America, there are two groups of cedars. The juniper trees are small shrublike trees often grown for decoration. The cedar trees of eastern North America include the Northern white cedar, Atlantic white cedar, Eastern red cedar, and the Southern red cedar. The cedars are small, evergreen trees that grow in a cone shape. (*See* EVERGREEN.)

Cedars are found in many different types of places. Atlantic white cedars are commonly found in swamps. Eastern red cedars can be found growing in old pastures. The wood of cedar trees is very strong. It rots very slowly, which also makes it a good wood to build with. Cedar wood is often used in furniture, fence posts, shingles, and poles. *See also* ARBORVITAE; SUCCESSION.

S.R.G./M.H.S.

CELERY (sel′ ə rē) Celery (*Apium gra-veolens*) is a biennial plant in the parsley family. Native to the Mediterranean area, celery has an edible stem that grows above the ground. The edible parts of a celery plant are cooked or eaten raw. In ancient China, celery was used as a medicine. The top of a celery plant has delicate leaves and small flowers. The seeds of the celery plant are used as a spice. Gray brown and about .25 cm [.1 in] long, celery seeds are among the smallest seeds of all the cultivated plants. A variety of celery called celeriac has a large root used as a vegetable. In Europe, a poisonous variety called wild celery grows in swamps near the sea. If the stems of wild celery are covered with soil to keep out the light, they will turn white and can be eaten.

G.M.B./F.W.S.

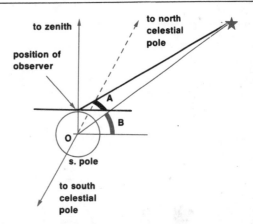

The center of the celestial sphere is the center of the earth. The altitude (A) measured by an observer on earth is slightly different from the geocentric altitude (B)—the altitude as measured from the center of the earth.

CELESTIAL SPHERE (sə les′ chəl sfir′) The celestial sphere is used by astronomers to describe the positions of stars. It is an imaginary sphere of indefinite radius, having the earth as its center. The points where the earth's axis, if continued into outer space, passes through the celestial sphere, are called the celestial poles. The celestial equator is the circle where a plane (flat surface) through the earth's equator meets the celestial sphere.

A point on the earth can be described by its latitude and longitude. Points on the celestial sphere are described in a similar manner. Celestial latitude is called declination. Declination is measured from the celestial equator the same way latitude is measured from the

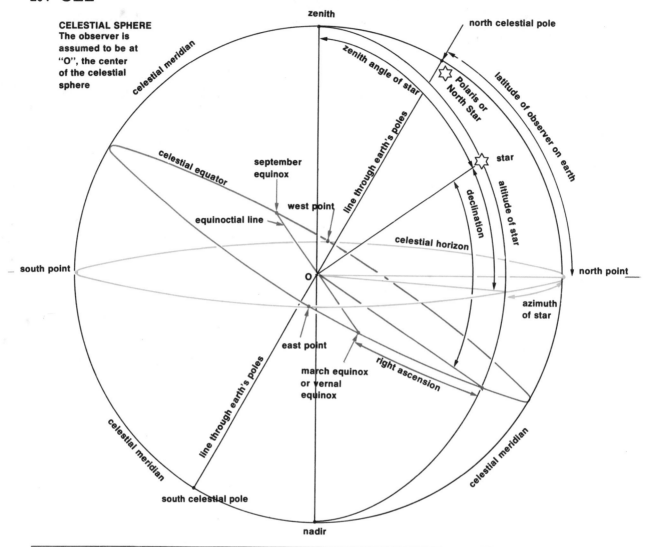

CELESTIAL SPHERE
The observer is assumed to be at "O", the center of the celestial sphere

Labels in diagram: zenith, north celestial pole, celestial meridian, zenith angle of star, Polaris or North Star, latitude of observer on earth, celestial equator, september equinox, star, west point, line through earth's poles, declination, altitude of star, equinoctial line, celestial horizon, south point, O, north point, azimuth of star, east point, right ascension, march equinox or vernal equinox, celestial meridian, celestial meridian, south celestial pole, nadir

The celestial sphere, above, is an imaginary sphere that astronomers use to define the positions of stars. The earth is considered the center of the celestial sphere. The points where the earth's axis passes through the sphere are called the celestial poles. Instead of latitude and longitude, astronomers use the measurements declination and right ascension.

earth's equator. Celestial longitude is called right ascension. The longitude of the earth is measured from the Greenwich meridian. In a similar way, right ascension is measured from the vernal equinox. The vernal equinox is the point where the sun crosses the celestial equator at the beginning of spring in the northern hemisphere.

There are other important points on the celestial sphere. The zenith is the point directly above the observer. The nadir is the point directly opposite to the zenith on the celestial sphere. The celestial horizon is the circle that passes midway between the zenith and the nadir. The points where the celestial equator and the celestial horizon cross are called the east and west points. The celestial meridian goes through the zenith, nadir, and celestial poles. The points where the meridian crosses the horizon are the north and south points.

Astronomers use the celestial sphere to help explain the positions of heavenly bodies, and as an aid in plotting maps of the heavens.

J.M.C./C.R.

CELL

The cell (sel) is the basic unit of life. All living organisms—plants, animals, and Protista—are made up of one or more cells. (*See* PROTISTA.) The only possible exception is the virus. Viruses are acellular (not made of cells), but scientists are divided on the issue of whether a virus is a living organism. (*See* VIRUS.) Some cells, such as the yolk of an egg, are large enough to be seen with the naked eye. Most cells, however, are microscopic in size, and can only be seen with the aid of a microscope. (*See* MICROSCOPE.)

Some organisms consist of only one cell. This cell carries on all the functions of life (gas exchange, intake of food, excretion of wastes, growth, reproduction, and death). These one-celled organisms may live alone or in groups. Most organisms, however, are made up of many cells. The human body, for example, contains more than 10 trillion cells. In multicellular organisms, groups of cells are specialized to perform specific functions. A group of cells gathered together to perform a single function is a tissue. A group of tissues gathered together to perform related functions is called an organ.

History In the 17th century, the first microscopes were developed. (*See* LEEUWENHOEK, ANTON VAN.) For the first time, scientists were able to look "inside" an object—beyond the outside features and into its internal structure. In 1665, Robert Hooke, an English scientist, looked at a piece of cork under a microscope. (*See* HOOKE, ROBERT.) He noted that cork was made up of many tiny, boxlike structures. Hooke called these structures "cells." In 1838, the German scientists Matthias Schleiden and Theodor Schwann proposed the cell theory. The cell theory states that all living things are made of cells.

Cell structure Cells vary greatly in shape and size. The shape of a cell is usually related to its function. For example, an ameba cell has no particular shape. It is a jellylike blob that changes shape as it moves. Some muscle cells are long and thin, allowing them to contract when doing work. Cells vary in size from the tiniest, a bacteria cell measuring 0.0005 cm [0.0002 in] long to the largest, an ostrich egg yolk measuring 7.6 cm [3 in] long. Most cells, though, are about 0.0025 cm [0.001 in] long. The size of a multicellular organism depends on the number of cells and not the size of the cells.

In spite of the variations in shape and size, all cells have the same basic structure. All cells are enclosed in an outer "skin" that is usually called a cell membrane (or plasma membrane). The cell membrane holds the cell together and separates it from its surroundings. The cell membrane is semipermeable—that is, it allows some substances through but refuses others.

Within the cell membrane is the protoplasm. The protoplasm includes the nucleus and the cytoplasm with its organelles.

The nucleus is frequently called "the control center of the cell" because it directs most of the cell's activities. The nucleus is enclosed by a nuclear membrane which, like the

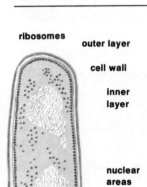

ribosomes
outer layer
cell wall
inner layer
nuclear areas
cell membrane

Left, the cell of a bacterium. Bacteria have simpler cells than those of animals and plants. For example, bacterial cells have no mitochondria—the energy producers of the cell (see diagram page 266).

cell membrane, is semi-permeable. Cells which contain a nucleus surrounded by a nuclear membrane are called eucaryotic cells. The nucleus contains special structures called chromosomes. (*See* CHROMOSOME.) The chromosomes contain genes which control the heredity of the cell. (*See* GENE.) Basically, the genes control the production and functioning of enzymes which, themselves, control the chemical processes within the cell. The nucleus may also include one or more nucleoli. The nucleoli help produce ribosomes. Some cells such as bacteria, some algae, and red blood cells, do not have a well-defined nucleus. They are called procaryotic cells. Their nuclear material is suspended in the cytoplasm.

The cytoplasm is everything in the cell between the cell membrane and the nuclear membrane. (*See* CYTOPLASM.) The cytoplasm is made up of a watery liquid and several structures called organelles. There are usually several substances such as enzymes and digested food which are dissolved in the cytoplasm. The organelles include mitochondria, endoplasmic reticulum, ribosomes, lysosomes, centrioles, chloroplasts, and Golgi bodies, for example.

Most cells have one or more mitochondria. The mitochondria are the "power houses" of the cell and produce most of the energy needed for cellular activities. (*See* ATP; MITOCHONDRIA.) The endoplasmic reticulum is a series of membrane-enclosed tubes between the cell membrane and the nuclear membrane. Ribosomes are tiny, ball-shaped structures that are the sites of protein synthesis. (*See* RIBOSOME.) The ribosomes are composed of RNA and proteins. Lysosomes are small, enzyme-containing structures which help break down many substances such as food and, in the case of white blood cells, bacteria. The centrioles are two rod-shaped structures that are active in cell reproduction. The Golgi bodies store and release various substances from the cell.

Plant cells contain several additional structures. They have a strong cell wall surrounding the cell membrane. The cell wall usually contains cellulose, and gives plants additional support and protection. The cytoplasm of plant cells also contains organelles called chloroplasts, chromoplasts, and leucoplasts. Chloroplasts contain chlorophylls, the green pigments needed for photosynthesis. (*See* CHLOROPHYLL.) Chromoplasts contain pigmented substances other than chlorophyll. Leucoplasts are usually white or clear and are used to store starch. Most plant cells, and some animal cells, also contain vacuoles. (*See* VACUOLE.) Vacuoles are fluid-filled spaces in the cell that transport various materials within the cytoplasm.

Cell growth and reproduction   Cells can grow in size only a little. The growth of multicellular organisms (plants and animals) is caused by an increase in the number of cells. The cells of an elephant, for example, are about the same size as (though much more numerous than) those of a mouse. Cells usually increase in number by splitting in two by a process called mitosis. (*See* MITOSIS.) In mitosis, a parent cell produces two daughter cells which are identical in appearance and genetic structure to the parent. Once a cell has divided, the daughter cells usually begin to specialize so they can perform specific functions. In one-celled organisms, this process is a type of asexual reproduction called fission. (*See* ASEXUAL REPRODUCTION.)

Cells sometimes divide in a process called meiosis. (*See* MEIOSIS.) In meiosis, a parent cell divides twice, producing four daughter cells. Each of these daughter cells has half the number of chromosomes of the parent cell. Meiosis is characteristic of the production of gametes, or sex cells. (*See* GAMETE.) In sexual reproduction, a male gamete (sperm) joins

Facing right, various animal and plant cells. These cells have many more parts, or organelles, than bacteria cells.

PARTS OF ANIMAL AND PLANT CELLS

The cell membrane. Food can pass through it

Endoplasmic reticulum, other membranes within the cell

Ribosomes on the reticulum are where proteins are made

Mitochondria, the energy producers of the cell

Lysosomes, packets of enzymes that digest food

Microtobules, part of the reticulum

The nucleus contains the chromosomes and nucleolus

The centriole produces cell hairs (cilia) in many cells

The Golgi apparatus, where proteins collect

Vesicles, tiny "packets" that carry food around

Fat globules, stored food found in animal cells

Chloroplasts, concerned with photosynthesis

Chromoplasts, other pigment bodies coloring plant cells

Starch grains, stores of food in plant cells

Crystals, often found in the cytoplasm and vacuole

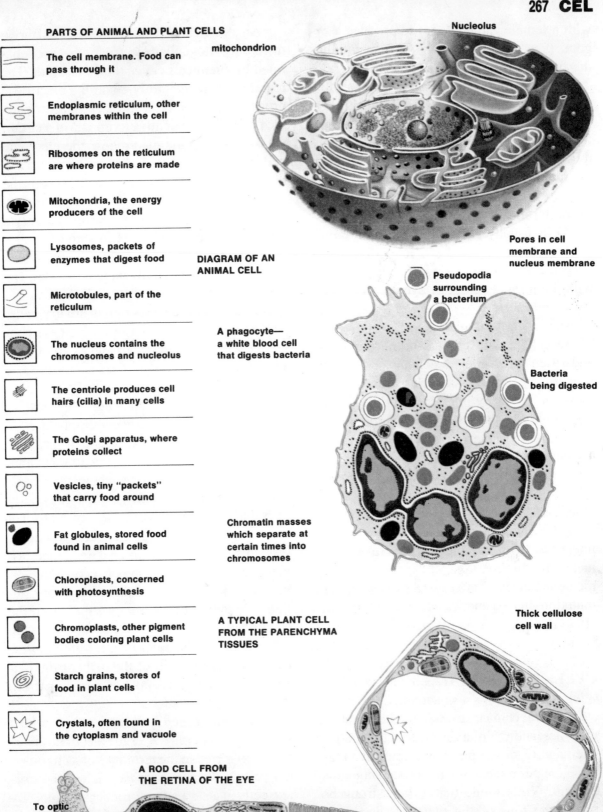

Nucleolus

mitochondrion

DIAGRAM OF AN ANIMAL CELL

Pores in cell membrane and nucleus membrane

Pseudopodia surrounding a bacterium

A phagocyte— a white blood cell that digests bacteria

Bacteria being digested

Chromatin masses which separate at certain times into chromosomes

A TYPICAL PLANT CELL FROM THE PARENCHYMA TISSUES

Thick cellulose cell wall

A ROD CELL FROM THE RETINA OF THE EYE

To optic nerve

Bags of membranes

with a female gamete (egg) to produce a zygote. (*See* FERTILIZATION.) This zygote has the full number of chromosomes.

Cell diseases Cells, like all living things, grow old and die. Some cells live for only a few minutes while others may live for hundreds of years. In the human body, cells die at the rate of about 3 billion per minute. These cells are replaced, however, by new cells produced by mitosis.

Cells usually grow, function, and reproduce in an orderly and efficient way. There are certain diseases, however, which interfere with the normal course of events. In cancer, some cells seem to go wild and reproduce in unusually large numbers. (*See* CANCER.) These cells are different from normal cells, and often have altered genetic codes. The cancerous cells exist in such great numbers, however, that they interfere with the normal functioning of the other cells. Some viruses kill cells by interfering with the normal hereditary material (DNA) in the cell. As the virus reproduces, it destroys the host cell, releasing hundreds of new viruses to attack other cells.

If the chemical reactions within a cell are interfered with or altered, the result is a metabolic disease. (*See* METABOLISM.) Many metabolic diseases are caused by a change, or mutation, in the genetic code. (*See* HEREDITY; MUTATION.) *See also* CYTOLOGY.

A.J.C./E.R.L.

CELL, ELECTRICAL An electrical cell (i lek′ tri kəl sel′) is a structure used to generate electrical current. In 1800, the Italian physicist Alessandro Volta discovered that certain chemical reactions produce electricity. Placing a copper rod and a zinc rod in a container of acid, Volta found that a wire strung between the tops of the two rods carried an electric current. This was the first electrical cell, or combination of chemicals to produce electricity. (*See* BATTERY.)

An electrical cell basically consists of two different plates called electrodes that are separated by chemicals called the electrolyte. The reaction of the electrolyte and the electrodes produces electricity at the electrodes. When the positive and negative terminals of a circuit are attached to the electrodes, the electrical cell provides a flow of electrons, or current, through the circuit. In some electrical cells the electrolyte is a liquid. These cells are called wet cells. Other cells have a solid electrolyte and are called dry cells. The standard automobile battery is a series of wet cells, which are similar to the cell invented by Volta. The batteries used to supply electricity for flashlights and transistor radios are dry cells. Dry cells usually consist of a zinc case containing a paste of chemicals and a carbon rod. The case and the rod are the electrodes. The paste of chemicals is the electrolyte.

Cells like those of the automobile battery can be recharged, or receive a supply of electricity after they have discharged or lost their charge. The cell of a flashlight battery cannot be recharged, because its chemicals finish reacting together and change into other chemicals that do not produce electricity. Cells that can be recharged are called secondary cells. Cells that cannot be recharged are called primary cells. The recharging of secondary cells involves the reversing of their chemical reactions. A source of electricity supplied to the electrodes causes the electrolyte to take on rather than give off electrons. In automobiles, the chemical reaction of the cells of the battery is reversed by a supply of electricity from the generator, or alternator.

All electrical cells produce voltage, which supplies current only after the electrodes have been connected to the terminals of a circuit. A dry cell produces 1.5 volts. Each of the storage cells in a car battery produces 2 volts. By connecting cells in a series, higher voltages are obtained. The 12 volt car battery consists of six two-volt cells. All cells provide direct current.

Today, scientists are experimenting with new kinds of electrical cells called fuel cells and solar cells, which have been used in satellites and space travel. In the fuel cell the electrolyte and electrodes are constantly replaced or renewed by the chemical combination of oxygen with hydrogen, or a hydrocarbon fuel. The solar cell is a semiconductor that produces electricity when struck by sunlight. *See also* PHOTOELECTRIC EFFECT. G.M.B./L.L.R.

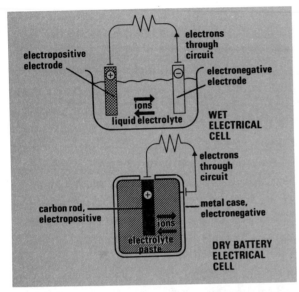

Simplified diagrams of wet and dry electrical cells are pictured above. Top, a wet cell. The electrodes, usually metals, are partly immersed in an electrolyte—a solution that conducts electricity. When the electrodes are connected, electricity flows between them. Electrons flow from the more electronegative metal to the more electropositive metal. To complete the circuit, electrically charged ions flow between the electrodes in the electrolyte. Bottom, the dry cell. The negative electrode is the metal case and the electrolyte is a paste.

CELLOPHANE (sel′ ə fan′) Cellophane is a thin, flexible material that resists moisture. Most cellophane is transparent and either colorless or slightly tinted. Cellophane that is not transparent may have any color. In 1908, Jacques Brandenberger, a Swiss chemist, invented cellophane. It is made from cellulose, which comes from plants.

Cellulose is obtained from wood fibers by a chemical process. Cellulose is then mixed with carbon disulfide. This mixture is dissolved in sodium hydroxide, forming viscose, a sticky liquid. Viscose is shaped into a thin sheet, then placed in sulfuric acid. The acid changes the sheet into cellophane. The cellophane is then dipped into liquids. These liquids remove impurities from cellophane and make it flexible. Manufacturers coat cellophane with a substance, such as synthetic resin, to make the cellophane moistureproof.

Most cellophane made in the United States is used to package products that need protection from moisture. Transparent cellophane protects cigarettes, candy, snack foods like potato chips and pretzels, and many other products. Cellophane is sometimes laminated (stuck) to aluminum foil or paper to make special wrapping materials. Cellophane is also used in the manufacture of drinking straws, envelopes, ribbons, and in tapes used for sealing and mending. J.J.A./J.M.

CELLULOID (sel′ yə loid′) Celluloid was the first artificial plastic to be widely used. Called cellulose nitrate by chemists, the plastic burns very easily. In 1869, John Wesley Hyatt, an American printer, invented Celluloid. It is made by treating cotton linters with a mixture of nitric and sulfuric acids. Cotton linters are the short fibers that stay on the cotton seed after the long ones have been removed. Pure cellulose nitrate is much too brittle for use as a plastic. It is combined with camphor to make it easier to bend and mold.

Cellulose nitrate plastics can be made to look like amber, onyx, ebony, and many other materials. Celluloid is now being used in products such as eyeglass frames, piano key coverings, and table tennis balls. Once used to make thousands of products, celluloid has been replaced by plastics that do not burn as easily. J.J.A./J.M.

CELLULOSE (sel′ yə lōs′) Cellulose is the substance that makes up most of the cell walls of many plants. It gives strength to a plant's leaves, roots, and stem, and makes them rigid. Cellulose is a carbohydrate, being made of carbon, hydrogen, and oxygen. Plants make cellulose from sugars. These sugars are built up from carbon dioxide and water in the process of photosynthesis. Cotton and flax fibers are almost all cellulose. Wood is about one-half cellulose. Paper is almost entirely cellulose. The substance is also present in all plant foods such as vegetables and fruit.

Cellulose is important to digestion. It makes up the bulk and roughage that aid the movements of the intestines. Cellulose helps to prevent disorders such as constipation.

Cellulose reacts with several strong acids and alkalis. When ordinary paper is placed in a strong solution of sulfuric acid, the cellulose in the paper swells. It forms a hard, waterproof paper used for legal documents, maps, and diplomas.

Cellulose is one of the most widely used chemical substances. It is especially used in the manufacture of explosives and many plastics. *See also* CELLULOSE ACETATE; CELLULOID; CELLOPHANE; RAYON.

J.J.A./E.R.L.

CELLULOSE ACETATE (sel′ yə lōs′ as′ ə tāt′) Cellulose acetate is a substance made from cotton linters, which are short cotton fibers. These linters, made chiefly of cellulose, are treated with acetic acid, acetic anhydride, and sulfuric acid. Sulfuric acid acts as the catalyst. When the reaction is complete, the mixture is added to water. Cellulose acetate separates as white flakes. The flakes are dissolved in acetone. This solution is then pumped through small holes in a device called a spinneret, where the acetone evaporates in warm air. The cellulose acetate comes out of the spinneret in the form of long fibers. Plasticizers and solvents are often added to cellulose acetate to make the fiber more flexible and useful. Dyes may be added to color it.

Cellulose acetate has replaced celluloid in

many instances. Celluloid burns too easily. Cellulose acetate is used in bulk form as a plastic. Knife and toothbrush handles are familiar objects made from cellulose acetate. The plastic is also used in making magnetic sound recording tapes, electrical insulation, and fireproof motion-picture film. The material is also used in thin sheets for wrapping various products. Cloth made from cellulose acetate fibers is silky, does not crease, and is easy to wash.

Cellulose acetate is used to make cellulose acetate butyrate. Because it stands up well under all weather conditions, cellulose acetate butyrate is often used in streetlight globes, automobile taillight covers, and outdoor signs.

J.J.A./J.M.

CELSIUS, ANDERS (1701–1744) Anders Celsius (sel′ si əs) was a Swedish scientist who invented the Celsius, or centigrade, temperature scale. Celsius introduced his scale in 1742. It is used throughout the world today and is part of the metric system of measurement. The Celsius scale is based on 0° for the freezing point of water and 100° for the boiling point of water. The Celsius scale is also called the centigrade scale because it is divided into 100 equal parts between 0° and 100°. Centigrade means "divided into 100 equal parts."

Celsius made many contributions to the field of astronomy. He was a professor at the University of Uppsala where he built the Uppsala Observatory. Celsius made many observations of the aurora borealis, or northern lights, and participated in an Arctic expedition that verified Newton's theory that the poles of the earth are slightly flattened. He wrote important works on the physical shape of the earth and measured the distance between the earth and the sun. *See also* CELSIUS SCALE.

W.R.P./D.G.F.

CELSIUS SCALE (sel′ sē əs skāl) The Celsius scale is a scale used to measure temperature. It is part of the metric system of measurement and is used throughout the world. The Celsius scale is based on 0° as the freezing point of water and 100° as the boiling point of water. The scale is divided into 100 equal parts between these two points. The Celsius scale is often called the centigrade scale. It was invented in 1742 by Anders Celsius, a Swedish scientist.

The Celsius scale has been used as the measurement of temperature throughout the world for many years. It is now slowly replacing the Fahrenheit scale as the common measurement of temperature in the U.S. The Fahrenheit scale is based on 32° as the freezing point of water and 212° as the boiling point of water. There are 180 divisions between the two points.

The formula for converting Fahrenheit temperature to Celsius temperature is: $°C = 5/9(°F - 32°)$. Thus, if the Fahrenheit temperature is 77°, the equation would tell us that $°C = 5/9(77° - 32°)$, or $5/9(45°)$, which equals 25°C. The formula for changing a Celsius temperature to a Fahrenheit temperature is: $°F = 9/5(°C) + 32°$. If the Celsius temperature is 20°, the equation would read: $°F = 9/5(20°) + 32°$, or $°F = 36° + 32°$, which equals 68°F.

Temperatures below the freezing point in the Celsius scale are given in minus degrees. The lowest temperature possible in theory is absolute zero. It is expressed as −273.15°C [−459.67°F.] *See also* THERMOMETER.

W.R.P./R.W.L.

CEMENT AND CONCRETE Cement (si ment′) in its broadest meaning is any substance that makes things stick together. Early people probably used sticky clay to hold together stones to make their houses. Common library paste and other kinds of glue are all forms of cement.

Concrete (kän′ krēt′) is a strong building material. It is made by mixing a cement with other materials. The use of concrete goes back thousands of years to the Egyptians and the Greeks. The ancient Romans made a concrete by mixing slaked lime with a volcanic ash. The result was called hydraulic concrete because it would harden underwater. Many of the buildings of ancient Rome, like the Colosseum, are still standing because they were made of solid concrete.

After the fall of the Roman Empire in the fifth century A.D., the art of making cement was lost until John Smeaton, a British engineer, rediscovered how to make it in 1756.

The most common kind of cement used in making concrete is called portland cement, or hydraulic cement. It is a fine gray powder made of limestone, silica, and alumina. The first portland cement was made by an Englishman, Joseph Aspdin, in 1824. He burned a mixture of one part clay to three parts limestone in a very hot oven, called a kiln, until the raw materials melted together to form a hard mass called a clinker. When the clinker cooled down, he ground it into a fine powder. He called the powder portland cement because it resembled a stone he had found on the Isle of Portland, England. Today, it is manufactured in a definite way so that it has become a standard product throughout the world.

Concrete is made by mixing cement with a fine aggregate, usually sand, a coarse aggregate, usually gravel, and water. The fine sand mixes with the coarse gravel, and the two are held together by the pasty mixture of cement and water. The materials must be mixed carefully in the right proportions. Too much water, for instance, makes a thin paste, and the hardened concrete is less durable.

Special techniques have been thought up so that the concrete can be mixed in large quantities at a central plant and then taken to the building site in specially designed trucks. The trucks have turning drums to keep the freshly mixed concrete from hardening along the way.

Concrete can stand up against strong pushing by other parts of a structure. We say it

Concrete columns (above) are set within wooden frames that are strapped with steel.

Concrete is poured from a truck to form a foundation.

Right, one of the tallest concrete buildings, in Australia.

is thus strong in compression. It is weak in tension, though, and may be pulled apart relatively easily. The tension of concrete may be increased by use of steel wires embedded in the concrete. The result is called reinforced concrete, which is used in many types of construction.

The United States produces more cement and uses more concrete than does any other country. P.G.C./A.D.

CENOZOIC ERA (sē′ nə zō′ ik ir′ ə) The Cenozoic era covers the last 65 million years of the earth's history. It is divided into two periods: the Tertiary period and the Quaternary period. The Tertiary period lasted approximately 63 million years. The Quaternary period covers the past two million years. The Tertiary period is further divided into five segments called epochs. The shorter Quaternary period is divided into the Pleistocene and Modern (or Holocene) epochs.

By the time the Cenozoic era began, most of the giant reptiles were extinct. Mammals became the dominant land animal, which is why the Tertiary period is often called the "age of mammals." Birds, insects, and flowering plants also evolved to a state similar to those of today. The Quaternary period saw the rise of human beings. (See EVOLUTION.)

The modern landscape took shape during the Cenozoic era. Tall mountain ranges, like the Rockies, Alps, and Himalayas, were formed.

During the later part of the Cenozoic era (Pleistocene epoch), widespread glaciation occurred as worldwide climatic patterns changed. As the earth warmed up again, the glaciers retreated (melted), forming many of the land features of Europe, Asia, and North America. See also ICE AGE.   J.M.C./W.R.S.

CENTAURUS (sen′ tȯr əs) Centaurus is a southern constellation that contains many bright stars. One, Alpha Centauri, is the third brightest star in the night sky. Another, Beta Centauri, is the tenth brightest star. Together, these two stars are called the southern pointers, because they point to the Southern Cross. Alpha Centauri is the star closest to the sun, about 4.3 light-years away. It has nearly the same size and brightness as our sun.

Another star in the Centaurus constellation is Proxima Centauri. This star revolves around Alpha Centauri and Beta Centauri, forming what astronomers call a triple star. Also seen in the Centaurus constellation is a cluster of thousands of stars called Omega Centauri.

Centaurus gets its name from ancient Greek myths about centaurs, imaginary creatures that were half human and half horse.
     J.M.C./C.R.

CENTER OF GRAVITY (sen′ tər uv grav′ət ē) The center of gravity is that point where all the mass or weight of an object seems to be concentrated. It is also called the center of mass. If the object is symmetrical, such as a coin or a ruler, the center of gravity is at the midpoint or center of the object. (See SYMMETRY.)

The position of the center of gravity is important in the balance of an object. If the center of gravity is directly over the base of an object, the object will not wobble. If the object is at an angle so that the center of gravity is not above the base, the object may fall. An object with most of its weight at the bottom, like a telephone, has a low center of gravity and cannot easily be tipped over. An object like a floor lamp, which has the weight of the shade and bulb at or near the top, has a high center of gravity and can be easily knocked over. It is important that automobiles and ships be designed with a low center of gravity to prevent them from overturning.   J.M.C./R.W.L.

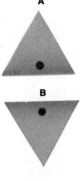

Object stability depends on the position of its center of gravity. (A) is stable. (B) is unstable. (C) has the same stability in any position because its center of gravity is central.

CENTIGRADE SCALE See CELSIUS SCALE.

CENTIMETER-GRAM-SECOND SYSTEM

The centimeter-gram-second (sent' ə mēt'ər gram' sek' ənd) system was the first system of metric units used by scientists. It has now been replaced by another metric system, called SI units. SI is the short way of writing Système International (French for International System).

The centimeter-gram-second system is often written cgs system, for short. In the cgs system the three basic units are the centimeter for length, the gram for mass, and the second for time.

Other units are developed from these basic units. For example, the cgs unit of force is the dyne. One dyne is the force needed to increase the speed of a mass of one gram by one centimeter per second for each second that the force acts. The cgs unit of energy is the erg. One erg is the work done when a force of one dyne acts through a distance of one centimeter. The erg is a very small unit. Ten million ergs are equal to one joule. The joule is the SI unit of energy. *See also* FOOT-POUND-SECOND SYSTEM. M.E./R.W.L.

CENTIPEDE

(sent' ə pēd') The centipede is a worm-shaped arthropod belonging to the class Chilopoda. There are more than 3,000 known species, mostly varying in size from 2 to 5 cm [1 to 2 in], but some tropical centipedes reach 30 cm [12 in]. They are found throughout the world in cool, damp places.

The head has a pair of antennae and three pairs of mouth-parts. The body is segmented, each segment having a pair of legs and usually one pair of spiracles. Most centipedes have 15-23 segments, but some have more than 100. The legs on the first segment are modified to form fangs. These fangs are called "poison claws" because they are filled with poison. This poison is injected into prey such as insects, worms, mollusks, and even other centipedes.

Centipedes live in the soil under rocks or logs. If disturbed, they can inflict painful bites on human beings. Some species of centipedes are bioluminescent. (See BIOLUMINESCENCE.) *See also* MILLIPEDE. A.J.C./C.S.H.

The centipede (above), a long-bodied arthropod, lives in the soil and captures its prey with its poison fangs. The larger species can inflict painful bites on humans. Centipedes vary in size from 2 to 5 cm [1 to 2 in]. However, some tropical centipedes reach 30 cm [1 ft]. They live throughout the world.

CENTRAL HEATING

(sen' trəl hēt' ing) Central heating is a system for warming a large area, such as a house, from one source of heat. The heat is delivered where it is needed. Most central heating systems serve only one building. Some, however, heat several buildings, such as those at an apartment complex.

There are two main types of central heating systems. A direct system moves warm air throughout the area being heated. An indirect system carries steam or hot water through pipes to convectors or radiators, which give off heat. Both systems use electricity or a type of fuel, such as oil or gas, as a source of heat.

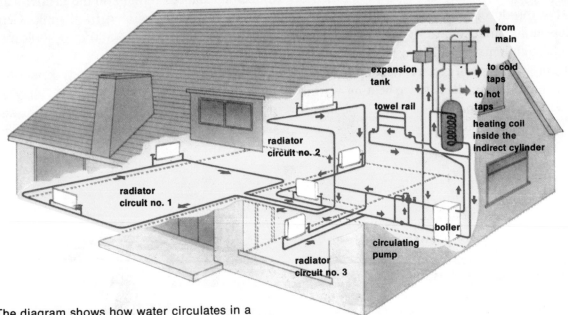

from
main

expansion
tank

to cold
taps

to hot
taps

towel rail

heating coil
inside the
indirect cylinder

radiator
circuit no. 2

radiator
circuit no. 1

boiler

circulating
pump

radiator
circuit no. 3

The diagram shows how water circulates in a small-bore hot water system of central heating. This indirect heating system carries hot water through pipes to radiators, which give off heat. A direct heating system moves warm air to heat an area. Both direct and indirect heating systems need fuel as a source of heat.

In central heating systems, the temperature can be controlled by one or more thermostats. The thermostat has a bar made of two different metals. Each metal expands when warm and contracts when cold, but at different rates. When the air warms, one metal expands more than the other. This makes the bar bend in one direction far enough to touch an electrical contact and shut the furance off.

In a steam heating system, the steam moves through pipes to one or more radiators. In a radiator, the steam condenses to form water. (*See* CONDENSATION.) As the steam condenses, it releases heat. This heat flows out to warm the surrounding air by convection. The cooled water is returned to the furnace where it is reheated into steam. The radiators in a steam heating system have valves that allow the escape of air. In a hot-water heating system, hot water travels from the boiler to the radiators, where it passes on its heat to the surrounding air. In some systems, hot water passes through pipes coiled under the floor. In warm air heating, air is warmed in a furnace and then forced through a system of ducts, or pipes, to each room. Another system of ducts carries cool air from the rooms back to the furnace. Many homes have warm air systems. These systems do more than just heat the air. For example, with a humidifier, a forced warm air system adds moisture to the air, increasing the humidity throughout the home. The ducts and blower can be used as part of a unit for central air conditioning.

Radiant heating involves the use of a continuous loop of a hot water pipe or an electric cable. This pipe or cable may be installed on the floor, wall, or ceiling. Heat leaves the pipe or cable by radiation. Radiation does not directly raise the temperature of the air within a room. It affects only the objects it strikes. Radiation distributes heat more evenly than convection. All radiant heating systems limit the temperature difference between the floor and the ceiling to only a few degrees.

Electric heating differs from other central heating systems. It requires no fuel in the building being heated. The fuel used to produce the electricity is burned at an electric power plant that may be far away. Electric heat is produced by heating electric units. These units produce heat by passing electricity through a material that resists the flow of current. This type of electric heating is called resistance heating. Resistance heating warms a room in the same way as radiant heating.

A heating system that uses a heat pump operates much as a warm air system. But the heat pump uses a condenser, pump, and other equipment to get heat from outside air or the ground and pump it into the building. During the summer, a heat pump works in reverse. It cools a building by pumping heat from the inside to the outside.

Besides central heating, two very new methods of heating are earth heat and solar heat. In earth heating, cold air is carried in pipes through warm earth below the frozen ground. The air absorbs the warmth and carries it into the house. Solar heating uses the radiant energy from the sun directly. Solar energy not only provides warmth, but can also be used to run machines. Solar heating is not widely used at this time. Huge reflectors are needed to "collect" enough sunlight to heat large areas. Solar heating is likely to be the most common heating system in the future. The fuels required in central heating systems are extremely expensive and getting more scarce every year. *See also* FUEL; HEAT; SOLAR ENERGY. J.J.A./R.W.L.

CENTRIFUGAL FORCE *See* CENTRIPETAL FORCE.

CENTRIFUGE (sen′ trə fyüj′) The centrifuge is a device that spins around at high speed. It is usually an electric motor to which two or more containers are attached. When the motor is turned on, the containers spin around at high speed. The centrifuge is used to separate liquids that are mixed together, or solid particles that are mixed in a liquid. As it spins, the heavier liquid or solid particles move to the outside of a container, and the

lighter substances remain on the inside. This is how cream is separated from milk. Centrifuges can turn at from 800 to 6,000 times per minute.

Centrifuges are used in many scientific, industrial, and medical laboratories. They are used in the separation of blood serum and plasma. An ultracentrifuge is a centrifuge that can reach speeds of 80,000 turns per minute. J.M.C./J.T.

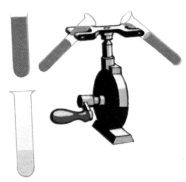

Above, a simple centrifuge. When the handle is turned, the test tubes whirl around. The centrifuge is used to separate liquids that are mixed together, or solid particles that are mixed in a liquid. As it spins, the heavier liquid or solid particles move to the outside of a container.

CENTRIPETAL FORCE (sen trip′ ət əl fōrs) Centripetal force acts to keep an object moving in a circle. According to Newton's first law of motion, a moving object travels in a straight line unless a force acts on it. (*See* DYNAMICS.) When a stone is tied to a string and swung around, the tension in the string supplies centripetal force that acts on the stone to keep it from moving off in a straight line.

An example of centripetal force is the gravitational force that keeps a satellite in orbit around its parent body, as our moon orbits the earth. In another example, a car traveling around a bend in the road is kept from skidding off by the centripetal force supplied by friction between the tires and the pavement.

According to Newton's third law of mo-

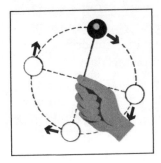

Left, the hand is acting as centripetal force, keeping the ball moving.

tion, every force creates an equal but opposite reaction. In the example of the stone and string, centripetal force is balanced by a force exerted by the string on the hand of the person holding it. This force is known as centrifugal force.

J.M.C./J.T.

CEPHALOPOD (sef′ ə lə pöd′) A cephalopod is a saltwater animal that belongs to the class Cephalopoda, in the phylum Mollusca. The octopus, squid, cuttlefish, nautilus, and ammonite belong to Cephalopoda.

Cephalopods (below) are soft-bodied creatures without bones. Most cephalopods are enclosed by a thick fold of skin called the mantle. The only living cephalopod with a shell is the nautilus. The cuttlefish has a chalky "cuttlebone" inside its mantle. The squid has a thin, horny plate. Most octopuses have no trace of a shell. Octupuses have eight tentacles, and squids have ten. Cephalopods can squirt an inky liquid into the water, which makes it cloudy and hard to see through.

Cephalopods are soft-bodied animals without any bones. A thick fold of "skin" called the mantle partly surrounds their bodies. In other mollusks, such as clams, the mantle produces a hard shell which encloses the body. The nautilus is the only living cephalopod with a shell. The cuttlefish and squids have a small trace of a shell inside their bodies, but the octopuses do not.

Cephalopods breathe with gills in the mantle cavity. After the water travels through the gills, it passes out through the siphon, a short spout. When this water is forced out of the siphon quickly, the animal will shoot backwards rapidly. Cephalopods use this method to escape from their enemies. They also squirt an inky liquid into the water which makes the water cloudy and hard to see through.

Although octopuses are often thought of as being dangerous, they rarely are. Most octopuses are very small, measuring only a few inches wide. They will swim away and hide if a diver comes near. Octopuses have eight legs, or tentacles, and live on the bottom of the ocean where they eat crabs and shrimp.

Squids are found in large numbers in the open sea. They have ten tentacles. They eat

octopus

ammonite

nautilus

squid

cuttlefish

crustaceans and small fish. Most squids are small, but the giant squid may reach lengths of 16 m [52 ft]. It has been known to fight a sperm whale. S.R.G./C.S.H.

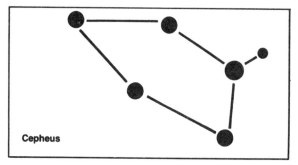

Cepheus is a constellation of dim stars in the northern hemisphere.

CEPHEUS (sē′ fyüs′) Cepheus is a constellation of dim stars in the northern hemisphere. A circumpolar constellation, it revolves around the pole star and is always above the horizon. Named after a king in an ancient Greek myth, the Cepheus constellation seems to form the outline of a house, or a triangle on top of a rectangle. In one of the corners of Cepheus is Delta Cephei, the famous variable star.

In 1784, the English astronomer J. Goodricke discovered that Delta Cephei varied in brightness, or pulsated, over a period of time. By determining that this star alternated between minimum and maximum brightness in 5.4 days, Goodricke established the study of variable stars, or stars that change in brightness. Goodricke's study of this star in Cepheus became the model for future study of similar variable stars, called Cepheid variables. Astronomers now know these stars pulsate because the gas envelopes that surround them become larger and smaller. By using information on the pulsation of a Cepheid variable, scientists are able to calculate its distance. *See also* STAR. G.M.B./C.R.

CERAMICS (sə ram′ iks) Ceramics are objects made from materials such as clay, feldspar, and flint that have been fired into permanent form. The word ceramics comes from the Greek word *keramos,* meaning "potter's clay." The term ceramic describes products that are made from materials other than a metal or a plastic.

Pottery is the oldest form of ceramics, dating back to prehistoric times. Examples of pottery more than 6,000 years old have been discovered in different parts of the world. The oldest way of fashioning clay into pottery was by a rotating wheel called the potter's wheel. Many new methods have since been developed. The development of pottery opened the door to the modern world of ceramics.

Most ceramics are compounds of silicon, carbon, oxygen, and nitrogen in combination with other elements. Clay and other materials used in ceramics form most of the earth's crust. These minerals, called silicates, are crushed and ground into fine particles. The particles are mixed and added to water. Water makes the particles plastic, or flexible, for shaping. Jiggering is a common method used to shape clay ceramics. In jiggering, a machine presses the clay into a spinning mold of the desired shape. Slip casting, another method, is done by pouring liquid clay into a mold. Some products, such as abrasives or insulators, are made by pressing the clay into a mold. Extrusion shapes bricks by forcing the clay through an opening in a shaping device. (*See* CASTING.)

After the product has dried, it is fired, or heated. This process takes place in a special type of furnace called a kiln. Ceramics are fired at temperatures ranging from 650°C [1202°F] to 1650°C [3002°F]. Firing hardens the product into permanent form. It also gives the product strength and durability.

Many ceramic products are coated with a glassy covering called a glaze. Glaze seals the surface and prevents the product from absorbing liquids. It also gives a smooth surface to the product and makes it easier to clean. Some glazes are used for decoration.

Ceramic materials are used to make a vast

Above, racks of unfired pottery are ready to be placed in a kiln, a special furnace. The kiln is used to harden pottery and give it strength and durability.

of ceramic products used for lining furnaces. Refractories resist heat and chemical action. Refractoriness is a term describing the ability of a material to withstand heat without softening or losing shape. Certain types of refractories are used for rocket nose cones, which must withstand the high temperatures caused by high-speed travel. Ceramic substances used in making refractories include alumina, magnesium compounds, and silica.

Experts in ceramics are continually developing new uses for their material. Different types of porcelain are used to make false teeth and artificial bone joints. Uranium oxide ceramics are used as fuel elements for nuclear reactors. Alumina is used in making certain lasers, which produce extremely strong light beams. J.J.A./J.M.

number of products. One important use is in making abrasives, which are materials used for grinding. Manufacturers use extremely hard ceramic materials, such as alumina and silicon carbide, for polishing and sanding many surfaces.

Clay and shale are used to make construction products, such as bricks and drainpipes. Cement is made chiefly of calcium silicates. (*See* CEMENT AND CONCRETE.) Gypsum is used in the manufacture of plaster. Bathtubs, sinks, and toilets are made of porcelain, which is made of clay, feldspar, and quartz.

Ceramics make excellent bowls, cups, and plates. In addition to not absorbing liquid, ceramics resist acids, salts, and extreme heat. Most ceramic dinnerware is made from a mixture of clay, feldspar, and quartz.

Some ceramic materials, such as alumina and porcelain, do not conduct electricity. These materials are useful as insulators in automobile spark plugs, electric power lines, and in television sets. Barium titanate is a ceramic material used in making capacitors.

The ceramic material silica is used in making a great number of glass products. (*See* GLASS.) The glasslike substance porcelain enamel is used as a protective coating on many metal products, such as refrigerators, stoves, and washing machines.

Refractories are another important group

Left, wheat is an important cereal crop of temperate climates. It is used in many foods.

Corn (below) is another important cereal crop. It was grown in North and South America more than 500 years ago.

CEREAL CROP (sir′ ē əl kräp′) Cereal crops are annual grains that are among the most important food plants. They have a high starch content and are a good energy source.

With the exception of buckwheat, all the cereal crops are members of the grass family. Cereal crops were cultivated as early as 5000 B.C. in Asia. They are now raised throughout the world. Farmers constantly try to improve the quality of their crops through genetic control. (*See* HYBRID.)

Cereal crops are grown for human use and animal use. Corn can be eaten cooked, or can be processed into flour, syrup, oil, or other forms. Once processed, corn can be used in many foods such as bread and breakfast cereals. Wheat is usually ground into flour and used for breads and other foods. Rice is the main food in the diets of half the people in the world. Most Asians rely on rice as their major food. The outer covering of rice, the husk, is rich in vitamins. (*See* BERIBERI.)

Rice, the chief cereal crop of Asia, is grown mostly in irrigated fields. Cereal crops were cultivated as early as 5000 B.C. in Asia. Rice is the main food in the diets of half the people in the world. It is the major food of most Asians. The outer covering of rice, the husk, is rich in vitamins.

Cereal grains used for animals are in the form of feed. About 65% of the corn grown in the United States is used for livestock feed. Mixed feed is made of one or more grains from cereal crops, vitamins, protein supplements, and drugs.

Cereal crops have many other uses. They are an important ingredient in many drugs, explosives, and alcoholic beverages. (*See* ALCOHOL; FERMENTATION.) *See also* BARLEY; MILLET; OAT; RYE; SORGHUM.

A.J.C./F.W.S.

CEREBELLUM (ser′ ə bel′ əm) The cerebellum is the second largest part of the human brain. It lies toward the rear of the cerebrum. It is concerned with the sense of balance, position of the body, and coordination of bodily movements. Certain animals that need good balance and coordination, like birds and mammals, have a larger, more developed cerebellum than fish and reptiles.

P.G.C./J.J.F.

CEREBRUM (sə rē′ brəm) The cerebrum is the largest part of the human brain. It is divided into two halves called cerebral hemispheres. The outer surface of the cerebral hemispheres is the cortex containing large numbers of nerve cells. These nerve cells receive messages from the sense organs, like the eye and the ear. The messages are used by the brain to send out signals to muscles and other organs of the body. Different parts of the cerebral hemispheres are called lobes. Cells in these lobes receive messages from various kinds of sense organs. For example, the temporal lobes are near the ears and serve as centers for hearing. The occipital lobes are centers for the sense of sight. P.G.C./J.J.F.

CERIUM (sir′ ē əm) Cerium (Ce) is a soft, gray metal belonging to the group of rare earth elements. In 1803, Jöns Berzelius, a Swedish chemist, discovered cerium. The metal was also discovered in the same year by Martin

Klaproth, a German chemist. The atomic number of cerium is 58. Its atomic weight is 140.1. Cerium has a melting point of 795°C [1,463°F] and a boiling point of 3,257°C [5,894.6°F].

Cerium is named after the asteroid Ceres which was discovered two years before the element. The metal is the most common of the rare earth elements. Found in many minerals, cerium is obtained for commercial purposes from the minerals monazite and bastnasite. Radioactive isotopes of cerium occur during the fission of plutonium, thorium, and uranium. Chemists use cerium to remove fission products from melted uranium.

Cerium is used to make alloys, especially misch metal. Misch metal, which easily produces sparks when struck, is often used to make flints in lighters. Cerium is also used to strengthen alloys. Cerium oxide is used for polishing glass and in the manufacture of porcelain. J.J.A./J.R.W.

CESIUM (sē′ zē əm) Cesium (Cs) is a soft, silvery white metal belonging to the alkali group of elements. In 1860, the German chemists Robert Bunsen and Gustav Kirchoff discovered cesium by observing its spectrum. The atomic number of cesium is 55. Its atomic weight is 132.9. The metal has a melting point of 28.5°C [83.3°F] and a boiling point of 678°C [1,252°F]. Cesium occurs in about seven out of every million parts of the earth's crust.

Cesium is used in making electronic tubes and photoelectric cells. (*See* PHOTOELECTRIC EFFECT.) Cesium ions, because they ionize readily and are heavy, may be used as a propellant to provide thrusts for rockets. *See also* IONS AND IONIZATION. J.J.A./J.R.W.

CHADWICK, SIR JAMES (1891–1974)
Sir James Chadwick (chad′ wik) was a British physicist who discovered the neutron, a part of the atom. He also discovered the existence of isotopes and played an important role in the development of the first atomic bomb during World War II.

In the early 1900s, scientists knew that the atom contained electrically charged particles called electrons and protons. Electrons are negatively charged, and protons are positively charged. They suspected that uncharged particles might exist in the atom. In 1932, Chadwick showed that radiation from the element beryllium, caused by the bombardment of alpha particles, is actually a stream of electrically neutral particles. He called these particles neutrons and pointed out that they were equal in mass, or weight, to protons.

Chadwick also explained the existence of isotopes. An isotope is a form of an element that is different from other forms of the same element. It contains a different number of neutrons in its nucleus and therefore has a different atomic weight. In 1935, Chadwick was awarded the Nobel Prize for physics for his discoveries.

Chadwick's discovery of the neutron, and research on chain reactions caused by nuclear fission, contributed to the development of the first atomic bomb.

Chadwick also spent several years working with Lord Ernest Rutherford on the transmutation of elements. This is the process whereby elements give off electrically charged particles known as alpha and beta rays. These change the makeup of the original atom in the element. Because of the changes, the new atom is of a different chemical element. Chadwick edited Lord Rutherford's paper in the 1960s. He also studied with Hans Geiger, the German nuclear physicist who invented the Geiger counter and who made important contributions to the understanding of radioactivity. *See also* ACCELERATOR, PARTICLE; ATOM. W.R.P./D.G.F.

CHAIN, ERNST BORIS (1906-1979)
Ernst Boris Chain (chān) was a German biochemist who discovered the healing properties of

neutron from
uranium 235 atom

uranium 235 atom

fission products—other
kinds of atoms

build-up of
fission products,
neutrons and
released energy

VIOLENT EXPLOSION

Above, diagram of a chain reaction in an atomic bomb. The bomb contains a metal that is radioactive—its atoms tend to break to release neutrons. These neutrons strike other atoms of the metal, causing them to split up to form fission products and more neutrons. Great numbers of neutrons are thus produced. A chain reaction often begins with nuclear fission. If the neutrons cannot escape from the surface of the metal then the released energy will cause the metal to explode violently.

In an atomic bomb explosion, the chain reaction is uncontrolled. The reaction builds up in a fraction of a second. A chain reaction can produce energy. This energy may be controlled and changed into electricity.

penicillin. Although it was Sir Alexander Fleming who discovered penicillin in 1928, it was Chain, working with Sir Howard Florey, who revealed its germ killing abilities. Chain and Florey performed the first clinical trials of the antibiotic in 1941. Chain, Florey, and Fleming were awarded the Nobel Prize for medicine in 1945.

In addition to his work on antibiotics, Chain also studied snake venoms, spreading factor (an enzyme that speeds up the flow of liquids through tissue), and insulin.

In 1961 Chain joined the faculty of the Imperial College, in London, England, as a professor of biochemistry.　W.R.P./D.G.F.

CHAIN REACTION (chān′ rē ak′ shən) A chain reaction is a reaction that triggers a series of other reactions. An example of a chain reaction is shown by ten dominoes standing in a row, one behind the other. The first is pushed to hit the second domino. The second domino hits the third domino. The reaction continues until all the dominoes fall.

A nuclear chain reaction begins with fission. Nuclear fission is the splitting of an atomic nucleus. When the atomic nucleus is split, a large amount of energy is released. Nuclear fission occurs, for example, when a neutron strikes an atom of uranium or plutonium. The atom breaks into two smaller atoms and produces more neutrons. Each of these neutrons may strike more uranium or plutonium atoms, producing still more neutrons. This continuous process is called a chain reaction. A chain reaction can produce a large amount of energy. This energy may be controlled and changed into electricity. An atomic bomb explosion is an example of an uncontrolled chain reaction.   J.M.C./J.T.

CHALK (chŏk) Chalk is a soft white or grayish form of limestone. It is composed largely of calcium carbonate. The calcium carbonate comes from the shells of the tiny ancient sea creatures called Foraminifera. Many chalk deposits contain bands of a harder substance called flint, a variety of quartz.

Many chalk deposits formed during the Cretaceous period, about 136 million years ago. The White Cliffs of Dover, a large chalk deposit in England, were formed during this period. Chalk deposits may also be found in South Dakota, Texas, and Alabama.

Although it is called chalk, blackboard chalk is actually made mostly of gypsum.
J.M.C./R.H.

The Shakespeare cliff is at Dover, England. It is part of the White Cliffs of Dover.

Chameleons are unusual lizards. They change color according to their background. If a chameleon sits in brown leaves, it turns brown. If it sits in a green bush, it turns green. A chameleon is a lizard that is able to move its eyes independently of each other. Because of this, it can look in two different directions at once. Most chameleons are small, sometimes reaching 20 cm [8 in] in length.

CHAMELEON (kə mēl′ yən) A chameleon is a lizard that belongs to the family Chamaeleonidae. There are over eighty species of chameleons. Most are found in Africa. Most chameleons are small, sometimes reaching 20 cm [8 in] in length. These small lizards are best known for their ability to change the color of their skin to match their surroundings. If a chameleon sits in a green bush, it turns green. If it sits in brown leaves, it turns brown. A chameleons is also able to move its eyes independently of each other. This allows it to look in two different directions at once. Chameleons are often kept as pets. *See also* CAMOUFLAGE.   S.R.G./R.L.L.

CHAMOIS (sham′ ē) The chamois (*Rupicapra rupicapra*) is a goatlike mammal with short, curved horns. It lives in the mountains of Europe and western Asia, spending summers near the snow-covered peaks. In the winter, the chamois moves down to the forests near the base of the mountain. The chamois is reddish brown and grows to a height of 75 cm [30 in] at the shoulder and a weight of 30 kg [66 lb].

Chamois live in bands of 10 to 15 members. They are able to make enormous leaps across ravines and from rock to rock. Chamois are hunted for their skins. These skins can be made into a very soft leather which is also called chamois. Soft, synthetic leathers and sheepskin are often sold as "chamois cloth." A.J.C./J.J.M.

CHARCOAL (chär′ kōl′) Charcoal is a black, brittle substance which is porous, or full of tiny holes. Charcoal consists mainly of impure, or amorphous, carbon and ash. Amorphous carbon is made of tiny particles of graphite, a pure form of carbon. Charcoal also has a small amount of impurities, such as hydrogen and sulfur compounds.

Charcoal is manufactured by heating plants rich in carbon or by heating animal remains, such as bones, in ovens that contain little or no air. As the substance is heated, most of the hydrogen, nitrogen, and oxygen in the substance escape. The end product is charcoal.

Wood charcoal, so called because it is made from wood, is the most common type of charcoal. It consists chiefly of carbon. It has some ash and impurities. Bone charcoal, also called boneblack, is made from animal remains, mostly bones. Bone charcoal is made up mainly of ash, along with some carbon and impurities. Activated charcoal is charcoal from which most of the impurities have been removed. It is made by treating charcoal with steam and air heated to at least 318°C [604.4°F].

Charcoal has many uses. It makes an excellent fuel. Many people burn charcoal briquettes in outdoor barbecues. Artists use wood charcoal for drawing. In powdered form, wood charcoal is used in filters and also in gunpowder. Bone charcoal is used in pigments, or coloring matter. These pigments are used in dyeing leathers and coloring inks and paints. Powdered forms of wood, bone, and activated charcoal are used to remove unwanted colors, flavors, and odors from gases and liquids. Charcoal performs these tasks by adsorption. (*See* ABSORPTION AND ADSORPTION.) Activated charcoal is the kind that best takes up other substances by adsorption. Activated charcoal is used in gas masks to adsorb dangerous gases. J.J.A./J.M.

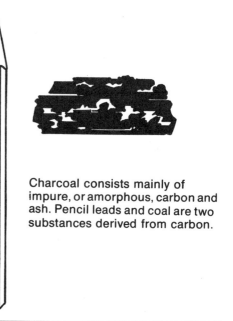

Charcoal consists mainly of impure, or amorphous, carbon and ash. Pencil leads and coal are two substances derived from carbon.

CHARGE (chärj) An electric charge is a natural unit of electricity. All atoms, the basic units of matter, are made up of particles called protons, electrons, and neutrons. Protons are particles with positive charge. Electrons are particles with negative charge. Neutrons are neutral particles, having no charge. The charge of an atom is determined by the ratio of electrons to protons. Since all matter is made up of atoms, all objects contain charged particles. Depending on the number of electrons and protons in its atoms, the charge of an object may be neutral, positive, or negative. An object has a negative charge when it has more electrons than protons. The charge is positive when there are fewer electrons than protons. When the number of electrons and protons is equal, the positive and negative charges cancel each other out, producing a neutral charge.

Objects with the same charge (both positive or both negative) repel one another. Objects with opposite charges (one positive and one negative) attract one another. The unit for measurement of a charge is the coulomb. *See also* BATTERY; CAPACITOR AND CAPACITANCE; ELECTROSTATICS.   G.M.B./J.T.

CHARLES' LAW Charles' law states that the volume a gas occupies under constant pressure varies with its absolute temperature, which is measured on a scale in which zero equals absolute zero ($-273.15°C$ or $-459.67°F$). Charles' law was formulated in 1787 by Jacques Alexander Charles, a French chemist. He did not publish his theory but explained it to another French chemist, Joseph Gay-Lussac. Gay-Lussac published the theory in 1802. Consequently, Charles' law is sometimes known as Gay-Lussac's law.

If the absolute temperature of a gas under constant pressure doubles, its volume also doubles. Similarly, if the absolute temperature decreases by a half, the volume decreases by a half. Gases become liquids or solids when their temperatures are lowered far enough.

A good example of Charles' law is the following. Place the open end of a balloon tightly over the top of an empty bottle. Use a rubber band to make a good, tight fit, if necessary. Apply heat from a lighted candle to the bottom of the bottle. The balloon will begin to fill with air as the air in the bottle expands, due to increased pressure caused by the heat. The expanding air escapes into the available space. *See also* AVOGADRO; BOYLE'S LAW; GAS.   W.R.P./J.T.

CHEETAH (chēt' ə) A cheetah is a large member of the cat family Felidae. It is found in Africa and southwestern Asia. Because of the black spots on its golden body, the cheetah can often be mistaken for a leopard. The two big cats can be told apart by the black line that runs from the cheetah's eyes to the corner of its mouth. Cheetahs also have a thinner body and longer legs. Unlike other cats, the cheetah has non-retractible claws. The claws always stay out, like those of a dog. Perhaps the best-known fact of the cheetah is its speed. It is the fastest animal on land. Cheetahs are able to run 112 kph [70 mph] while chasing antelope, its major prey. These cats can maintain these speeds only over very short distances. *See also* CAT.   S.R.G./J.J.M.

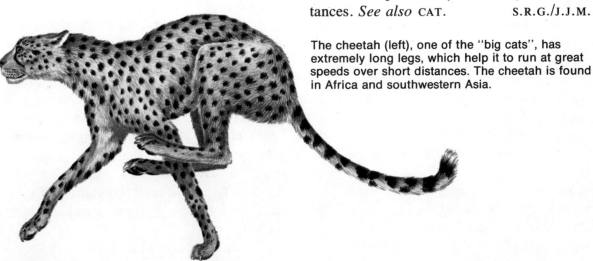

The cheetah (left), one of the "big cats", has extremely long legs, which help it to run at great speeds over short distances. The cheetah is found in Africa and southwestern Asia.

CHEMICAL ANALYSIS

CHEMICAL ANALYSIS (kem′ i kəl a nal′ ə səs) Chemical analysis is the way a chemist finds the identities and the amount of chemicals in a substance. There are two main kinds of chemical analysis. In qualitative analysis, a chemist tries to find out what elements and compounds various kinds of matter are made of. In quantitative analysis, he is concerned with how much of each element or compound is in various kinds of matter. Thus, if the chemist wants to know if salt contains iodine, he does a qualitative analysis. If he wants to know how much iodine, he does a quantitative analysis.

The methods used in qualitative analysis depend on whether the substance is organic or inorganic. Organic substances contain carbon. Inorganic substances do not. If a substance is inorganic, the various elements or groups of elements present can be identified by the way they react with certain test chemicals. There are special reagents that give certain reactions, such as a color change, with only one element or group of elements. If a substance is organic, analysis is more difficult. The general type of organic compound present can be identified by how it reacts with other chemicals. The actual compound is found by measuring a physical property, such as its melting or boiling point. The physical property must be different for each of the various compounds of one general type. The result must then be checked to see that no mistakes have been made. Chemists try to see if certain derivatives of the compound can be made. In this instance, a derivative is a compound obtained from another compound.

Quantitative analysis is done to find out the various amounts of an element or compound present in a substance. Inorganic substances are usually first dissolved to form solutions. (*See* INORGANIC CHEMISTRY.) The amounts of compounds present in the solutions may be found by measuring the strength of the solutions by volumetric analysis. Volumetric analysis is performed by reacting amounts of the solution and a test solution together. In this way, a chemist finds out how much of one solution is needed to react completely with a certain amount of the other. The amounts of compounds present in solution can also be found by precipitating (a way of removing) each compound from the solution as a solid. The solid is then separated, dried, and weighed. This method is called gravimetric analysis. In organic chemistry, each of the compounds present may have to be separated from the substance. The amounts of these compounds are measured. If the compounds cannot be separated, special derivatives of the compound may have to be made. The amounts of these derivatives are measured.

The methods of chemical analysis depend on the chemical makeup of the compounds being analyzed. Chemists today use certain machines to measure the physical properties of the compounds present. Different methods are used to identify certain physical properties. Mass spectroscopy is involved with the masses of atoms present. (*See* SPECTROSCOPE.) Chromatography is concerned with the amounts of the compounds that are absorbed by special substances. X-ray diffraction is analysis using X rays. Polarimetry is analysis of certain compounds using polarized light. Polarography is a technique in which analysis is performed using electrochemical methods. A specialized field of chemical analysis, called radiochemistry, has recently developed. Radiochemistry is the study of chemical processes by using radioactive materials.

Chemical analysis has many important uses. Food chemists must be able to identify and measure the amount of any impurities in food and drink. A forensic scientist working in crime detection depends on chemical analysis. He may work with amounts of substances that are so small they are nearly invisible. This type of work is called microanalysis.

Chemical analysis has wide use in industry. The purity of products in chemical industry must be constantly checked. Very often, small amounts of impurities can harmfully affect the usefulness of such products as metals, drugs, and plastics. In copper, for example, the presence of only .01% of phosphorus can greatly lower the quality of copper as an electrical conductor. Chemical analysis is also extremely important in medicine. Because good health is based on a healthy body chemistry, chemical analysis provides a valuable way to check and measure a person's state of health. Of great importance are the analyses of blood, urine, and stomach fluids to identify certain diseases. Such tests inform doctors how to treat diseases before they destroy a person's health. *See also* CHEMICAL INDUSTRY; CHEMICAL REACTION; MEDICINE.

J.J.A./A.D.

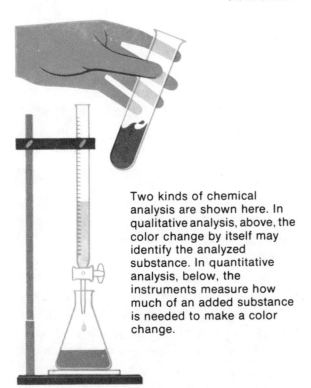

Two kinds of chemical analysis are shown here. In qualitative analysis, above, the color change by itself may identify the analyzed substance. In quantitative analysis, below, the instruments measure how much of an added substance is needed to make a color change.

CHEMICAL AND BIOLOGICAL WARFARE Chemical (kem′ i kəl) and biological (bī′ ə läj′ i kəl) warfare is the use of chemical and biological substances to kill or disable large numbers of people or to destroy their food supply. These weapons usually destroy life without harming property.

Modern chemical warfare began in World War I when chlorine gas was used by the Germans. Chlorine affects the lungs, causing choking and making it difficult to breathe. Gas masks were developed to keep the soldiers from breathing the gas. Chlorine disabled so many soldiers that the Germans devoted much more research to harmful gases.

Mustard gas was also used in World War I. It is absorbed through the skin, making gas masks useless. The gas causes blistering of the skin and irritation of the lungs. Although mustard gas is not related to mustard, their odors are similar. More soldiers died from mustard gas than any other. Nerve gas interferes with the normal action of the nerve cells and can cause convulsions, vomiting, and death. Many types of nerve gas are tasteless, odorless, and colorless. In World War I, more than 30% of the American casualties resulted from the use of gas.

Other gases, such as tear gas, have a temporary effect. Tear gas causes excessive crying, irritation of the nose, mouth, and eyes, and violent coughing. Tear gas is used in controlling crowds and riots.

Some chemicals are used to kill plants. These defoliants were widely used in the Korean and Vietnamese conflicts. Defoliants were sprayed on fields and jungles from airplanes and helicopters.

Biological warfare uses microorganisms like bacteria and viruses. It is sometimes called germ warfare. This type of warfare has been used for thousands of years.

Biological agents are highly infectious, resistant to sunlight and heat, and produce fast or long-lasting effects. It would be difficult to prove that a widespread sickness or disease was the result of biological warfare and not a natural epidemic. It is possible, therefore, that a country could launch a biological attack before an armed attack. This would have the effect of reducing the size of the army and lowering morale. It is possible that a few milliliters of certain microorganisms could destroy the entire population of the world.

In 1975, an international treaty banning biological warfare was approved. It prohibits production, possession, or use of biological agents. The 40 countries that signed the treaty are currently destroying stored biological agents.   A.J.C./J.M.

CHEMICAL COMBINATION, LAWS OF
The laws of chemical combination (kem' i kǝl käm' bǝ nā' shǝn) describe how atoms join together to form chemical compounds. Chemical compounds are atoms of the same or different elements joined together. The ratio in which atoms are present in a chemical compound depends upon the valence, or the ability of each element to bond with another.

Several rules apply to the ratios in which elements may combine to form chemical compounds. The law of constant proportions states that a certain compound always has the elements in the same ratio. For example, two atoms of the element hydrogen join one atom of the element oxygen to form the compound water. In any amount of water there is always twice as much hydrogen as there is oxygen.

The law of multiple proportions states that when two elements can combine to form more than one compound, they will always do so in a simple ratio. For example, the element carbon may combine with the element oxygen in more than one way. One atom of carbon may combine with one atom of oxygen to form carbon monoxide. One atom of carbon may also combine with two atoms of oxygen to form carbon dioxide. In both cases the atoms combine in simple ratios: one carbon atom for every oxygen atom in carbon monoxide and one carbon atom for every two oxygen atoms in carbon dioxide.   J.M.C./A.D.

CHEMICAL FORMULAS AND EQUATIONS
Chemical formulas (kem' i kǝl fòr' myǝ lǝz) and chemical equations (kem' i kǝl i kwā' zhǝnz) describe the makeup and reactions of chemical substances. Chemists use chemical symbols to stand for the elements. For example, the symbol for oxygen is O and the symbol for hydrogen is H. But not all the symbols consist of the first letter of the English name for the element. That would not be possible: there are 105 elements and only 26 letters in the alphabet. Some elements, therefore, have symbols consisting of two letters. For example, Cl stands for chlorine and Al stands for aluminum. In some elements, one or two letters from the Latin names for the elements are used. Na stands for sodium because the Latin for sodium is *natrium*. Au stands for gold because the Latin for gold is *aurum*.

To make up the formula for a chemical compound, chemists combine the symbols of the elements present. Water is a compound containing two atoms of hydrogen and one atom of oxygen. Its formula is H_2O. Table salt consists of one atom of sodium and one atom of chlorine. Its formula is NaCl.

Chemical equations use these symbols and formulas to show what happens when atoms and molecules react together. Hydrochloric acid is a common acid, with the formula HCl. Sodium hydroxide (also called caustic soda) is a common alkali, with the formula NaOH. When these two compounds are mixed together they react. This means that the atoms of one compound rearrange themselves with the atoms of the other compound. You can see this clearly in the equation. When hydrochloric acid reacts with sodium hydroxide, the atoms rearrange themselves so that table salt and water are formed.

$$HCl + NaOH = NaCl + H_2O$$

A chemical equation has to ''balance.'' That is, there must be the same number of atoms of each element on each side of the equation. If you count the number of atoms of hydrogen in this equation, you will see that there are two on each side.   M.E./A.D.

CHEMICAL INDUSTRY

Manufacturers involved in the production of anything made by chemicals make up the chemical industry (kem′ i kəl in′ dəs trē). An almost countless number of products are made by chemistry. By producing numerous chemicals, drugs, and materials, the chemical industry has brought about a change in our way of life.

A brief history Early developments in chemical industry came during the 1600s. Scientists such as Robert Boyle, Joseph Priestly, Antoine Lavoisier, and others led the way to modern chemistry and the chemical industry. In 1635, John Winthrop, Jr., started America's first chemical plant in Boston. He produced saltpeter for gunpowder and alum for tanning hides. Still, most of the chemicals used by colonists came from Europe. By 1900, many dyes and drugs were being manufactured in Germany, England, and France. Discoveries at this time included Bakelite res-

Below is a modern chemistry laboratory.

ins by Leo Baekeland, and synthetic, or artificial, ammonia by Fritz Haber.

The development of synthetic plastics and fibers came during the 1920s. Shortly after, the first petrochemicals were produced for commercial purposes. A petrochemical is any substance obtained from petroleum, such as gasoline. World War II sparked the American chemical industry to produce a great deal of war materials. Wartime use proved many synthetic materials to be as useful as, and sometimes more useful than, natural materials. After the war, there was a great demand for chemical materials such as nylon and synthetic rubber. The chemical industry has grown rapidly since World War II. The United States is now estimated to produce about 40% of the world's chemicals.

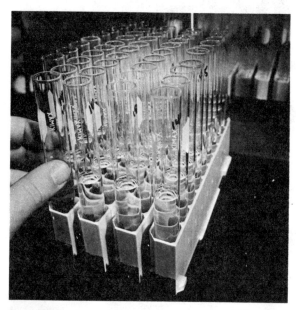

The products made by chemical industries must always be checked for quality before leaving the factory.

The branches of chemical products   There are three main branches of materials made by the chemical industry. One is basic chemicals, such as inorganic acids, alkalis, salts, and organic compounds. These chemicals are the starting materials for many products. The materials come from the air, earth, sea, and agriculture. Crude petroleum is probably the

most important raw material for basic chemicals. Crude petroleum provides more than half of the industrial organic chemicals. These include ethylene for antifreeze and xylene for paint and synthetic fibers. Limestone rock supplies lime used to make products from which acetylene gas is made. Furfural, made from corncobs, is a chemical often used in making plastics. The chemical industry gets magnesium from the sea and iodine from seaweed.

The second branch of chemical products is known as the intermediate chemicals. Intermediate chemicals include synthetic fibers, plastic materials, fats, and oils. Basic chemicals may be used by themselves or made into an intermediate chemical. All intermediate chemicals are eventually made into finished products. The basic chemicals urea and formaldehyde are reacted to make an intermediate chemical. This chemical is a synthetic resin. The resin can be molded into items such as handles and light fittings.

The third branch of chemical materials, the finished chemicals, include soaps, paints, cosmetics, drugs, and many other products. These products are ready for use in the home or in manufacturing.

The chemical industry does not just make and sell materials as finished products. It sells many products as raw materials to other manufacturers. In other words, one company's finished product is another's raw material. For example, one company may buy an anhydride from an anhydride maker in order to make a resin. A paint company may then buy the resin from that manufacturer in order to make paint.

Making chemical products   The first step in the manufacture of chemical products is research. Chemical research tries to satisfy the needs of various manufacturers. For

Right, a chemical plant by night. This plant makes carbon black, which is used for many purposes, including the rubber in tires.

example, an old type of putty dried up easily, cracked, and fell loose from windows. Research developed a synthetic-rubber putty that is many times stronger and resists weather much better than the old type. At one time, the best paint was made with lead and thinned with linseed oil. This paint had an unpleasant smell and dried very slowly. Research chemists invented new paints that can be mixed with water. Some of these paints dry in twenty minutes.

The next step in making chemical products is the obtaining of raw materials. Chemical companies try to locate near the raw materials they need. For example, factories that make petroleum are often set up near the oil fields of the southwestern United States.

The third step is in manufacturing. When a company decides to manufacture a product discovered by research, chemical engineers are needed. Chemical engineers break down the laboratory methods into certain steps of physical operations and chemical processes. Some physical operations put the raw materials into the desired form. Common physical operations include mixing, grinding, distillation, fluidizing, absorption, extraction, evaporation, drying, and filtration. (*See* FILTER.)

Mixing is usually a simple process. Sometimes large, complicated machines are used to mix and blend powders, liquids, and other substances. The object of grinding is to produce particles of a certain size. The ball mill grinder is made of a rotating drum that contains steel or flint balls. The balls reduce the size of the particles as they tumble over each other. Distillation is the separation of a mixture of liquids into different parts by boiling.

When a mixture of two liquids cannot be separated by distillation, extraction is used. (*See* SOLUTION AND SOLUBILITY.) Extraction is widely used in the organic chemical industry. For example, it is used to remove acetic acid from weak acetic acid solution. The solution is treated with ethyl acetate, which dissolves the acetic acid. This extract is then distilled so that pure acetic acid is obtained. Fluidizing is used for moving solids in a particle form. It is also used for keeping particles in suspension in a fluid.

Evaporation is one of the main ways to obtain substances dissolved in water. The most common evaporators are steam-heated. The steam passes through tubes in the solution. The hot solution gives off water vapor. Therefore the solution becomes more concentrated. If the dissolved substance could undergo a chemical change if heated too much, vacuum evaporation is used. In this system, the pressure above the liquid is reduced. This lowers the boiling point. (*See* BOILING AND BOILING POINT.)

Drying is often the last stage in the manufacturing of a product. Solids are often dried by blowing warm air over or through them in special types of driers. Watery mixtures are dried on steam-heated drums. These drums are constantly revolving. The watery mixture sticks to the surface of the drum. The drying takes place as the drum rotates. The dried mixture is then scraped off. A similar instrument is used in filtration. In filtration, the drum's surface has many holes in it and is covered with a filter cloth. The liquid is sucked through to the inside of the drum.

Chemical processes include esterification, which is the formation of an ester (a chemical compound) from the reaction of an acid and alcohol. Hydrolysis, the splitting of a compound into its parts by adding water, is also used. A common chemical process is polymerization, which involves making larger molecules out of smaller ones.

Before the chemical engineer builds a full-size plant, he makes a smaller pilot plant. A pilot plant may include common pieces of equipment, such as pumps, kettles, and filters. He makes tests and plans with this smaller equipment until he is satisfied with its performance. At this time, he may approve the construction of a large plant. A chemical engineer chooses large commercial equipment, such as the equipment already mentioned. Sometimes special equipment has to be designed.

Disposing of wastes is one of the basic problems in chemical production. Wastes are often the impurities separated from raw materials, intermediates, and final products. In 1974, the United States chemical industry spent more than $100 million to dispose of wastes in ways that do not pollute the air or bodies of water. For example, some detergents were polluting rivers and streams. The chemical industry developed various detergents that are quickly destroyed by bacteria. The chemical industry often works with federal, state, and local governments to solve waste problems. (*See* POLLUTION.)

Safety precautions play a very important part in the chemical industry. Most people believe that a chemical plant is a very dangerous place. Actually, people who work in these plants are relatively safe. When accidents do happen, the industry conducts research to find out the cause. In this way, they can prevent future accidents.

There are many different methods for distributing and selling chemical products. Huge amounts of basic chemicals are usually sent out by pipeline, railroad, or ship. Smaller amounts go in trucks. Manufacturers sell to wholesalers, agents, and other middlemen. Middlemen are people who take care of the needs of smaller customers. Middlemen buy in carload amounts. They then package the products and sell it in small amounts.

The importance of the chemical industry It is hard to imagine how important the chemical industry is. In the home, more than 25% of all textiles (woven material) are made from synthetic fibers. Chemical treatments make cotton and woolen materials almost wrinkle-free, water-repellent, and nearly shrinkproof. Synthetic fibers make up more than half of the rugs produced. Most of the fabrics used in furniture are chemically treated. Refrigerators cool food by means of synthetic substances that absorb heat. Many wallpapers and paints are chemically treated, which makes the products washable.

Chemical fertilizers help farmers produce larger crops. Many chemicals, such as insecticides and herbicides, protect crops from animal pests and plant diseases. Chemical solutions replace soil in hydroponic farming. (*See* HYDROPONICS.) Chemical feed supplements, which include antibiotics and hormones, improve the quality of livestock.

Almost every industrial manufacturer uses chemicals. In many cases, synthetic rubber has replaced natural rubber. Steel makers use oxygen to make steel and chemically to make metals for alloys. It is almost impossible to measure the growth in products that has developed from the chemical industry.

The industry's contribution in health has been mainly in the production of antibiotics, sulfa drugs, and vaccines. Most medicines and drugs are chemical products. Synthetic vitamins aid in nutrition. Water fluoridation helps reduce tooth decay.

In transportation, chemical industry produces alloys that make light and strong materials used in building trucks, cars, planes, ships, and trains. Crude petroleum is processed to give fuels, oils, gases, and petrochemicals. The most important fuels are jet fuel for planes and gasoline for automobiles. The average new automobile has about 61 kg [135 lbs] of plastic parts that are made from chemicals.

The chemical industry plays a key role in national defense. The industry produces the fuel that propels rockets, missiles, and airplanes. Chemical companies make synthetic fluids, such as silicone lubricants, for high-speed aircraft.

Tremendous chemical developments are happening every year. Such developments include tranquilizers for treating emotional disorders, many polyester fibers, new types of concrete, and scores of other products. Fifty years ago, few people knew what the chemical industry was. Today, their lives depend on it. *See also* CHEMISTRY, HISTORY OF.

J.J.A./A.D.

CHEMICAL REACTION (kem′ i kəl rē ak′ shən) A chemical reaction happens when elements and compounds react together to produce different compounds. Food changes in cooking. It also changes when people eat it. These are examples of chemical changes, or chemical reactions. Chemical reactions also occur when compounds break down into simpler compounds or elements. In chemical reactions, the atoms of elements change the ways in which they are joined to each other. The chemical nature of the substance taking part in the reaction changes. This change may be shown by a difference in the substance's appearance. Also, the substance may feel harder or softer. A chemical change is different from a physical change. If a change is purely physical, the chemical nature is not changed. But in a chemical change, physical changes may also occur.

There are four main kinds of chemical reactions. Combination, also called synthesis, takes place when two or more elements or compounds unite to form a new compound. For example, hydrogen (H) and oxygen (O) combine to form water. This can be written in a chemical form:

$$2H_2 + O_2 \rightarrow 2H_2O$$

Hydrogen has a strong affinity (attraction) for oxygen. Therefore, the two easily combine to form water.

Decomposition means the breaking down of a compound into two or more simpler compounds or elements. For example, if mercuric oxide (HgO) is heated, it decomposes into mercury and oxygen. A chemist shows this reaction by writing:

$$2HgO + heat \rightarrow 2Hg + O_2$$

Replacement, also called substitution, occurs when a compound loses some elements but gains others in their place. A replacement reaction between zinc (Zn) and sulfuric acid (H_2SO_4) produces zinc sulfate ($ZnSO_4$) and hydrogen (H_2).

$$Zn + H_2SO_4 \rightarrow ZnSO_4 + H_2 \uparrow$$

Because hydrogen is easily replaced in acids by metals, zinc and sulfuric acid produce hydrogen. Also, hydrogen is a gas. It rapidly leaves the test tube or wherever the reaction is taking place, as is shown by the upward arrow.

The fourth kind of reaction is called double decomposition or double replacement. This happens when two compounds exchange atoms or groups of atoms. For example, silver nitrate ($AgNO_3$) and sodium chloride (NaCl) in solution form silver chloride (AgCl) and sodium nitrate ($NaNO_3$).

$$AgNO_3 + NaCl \rightarrow NaNO_3 + AgCl \downarrow$$

Silver chloride is formed by double composition because it does not dissolve. All the other compounds are soluble, or dissolve. (*See* SOLUTION AND SOLUBILITY.) Silver chloride leaves the solution as a precipitate, as is shown by a downward arrow. It takes no further part in the reaction. Therefore the reaction continues in the same direction.

Not all reactions go completely in one direction. Often a balance or equilibrium is reached. In this instance, the reacting compounds and the products are all present in certain proportions (amounts). If one of the compounds or products is removed, as happened to silver chloride in the reaction described, the reaction goes in the direction that produces more of that substance. This goes on until the equilibrium is reached again.

The chemist (right) is making laboratory tests on lead.

Temperature, pressure, and other conditions can also affect the equilibrium and the direction of a reaction. This kind of reaction is called a reversible reaction. It can be made to go in either direction, depending on the conditions. *See also* CHEMICAL FORMULAS AND EQUATIONS. J.J.A./A.D.

CHEMISTRY (kem′ ə strē) Chemistry is the science of the elements. It deals with the properties and chemical reactions of the elements and their compounds. It also studies the way in which these elements and compounds can be made.

Many materials that we take for granted were first made by chemists. For example, plastics are chemical compounds that have thousands of different uses. Many drugs that are now used to fight illness are made by chemists. Synthetic fabrics, like polyesters, are the result of chemistry.

There are several branches of chemistry. Inorganic chemistry is the study of elements and compounds that are found in nonliving material. Organic chemistry is the study of carbon compounds. Many of them are found in living things. Physical chemistry studies how physical properties, such as heat and pressure, affect chemical reactions. A newer branch of chemistry is biochemistry. It studies the chemical reactions that occur in living things. M.E./A.D.

CHEMISTRY, HISTORY OF

Many years before chemistry (kem′ ə strē) became a science, people knew how to combine certain substances and change their shapes in order to make things. For example, by 2000 B.C., people of Egypt made bronze by melting tin and copper together. They also made special substances to make glass jewelry. Some craftworkers knew how to make perfume and wine. All of these objects involved the production and control of chemical changes. (*See* CHEMICAL REACTION.) However, the people at that time did not know why these changes took place.

The great thinkers, or philosophers, of China, India, and Greece formed the first theories, or systems of thought, about chemistry and the nature of matter. The Shu Ching, a Chinese book written about 350 B.C., claimed that all matter was made of earth, fire, water, metal, and wood. Empedocles, a Greek philosopher, believed there were four main "elements," namely earth, fire, water, and air. Democritus, a leading Greek philosopher, taught 2,300 years ago that all things were made of atoms. His idea was that atoms were hard pieces of matter so tiny they were invisible. This theory is based roughly on the same rule as the modern atomic theory of matter.

Alchemy and Arab chemistry Alchemy was one of the earliest forms of chemistry. It combined science, magic, philosophy, and religion. The alchemists tried many ways of changing substances into gold. They also tried to produce a substance that would give people a long and healthy life or let them live forever. Alchemists did little to advance an understanding of nature. But they did develop many useful chemical methods. They found ways of making chemical changes in many substances. Alchemists improved methods of taking metals from ore. They learned how to make and use various acids. They also designed laboratory equipment, such as balances, for weighing chemicals.

Alchemy took place mainly in Alexandria, a Greek city in Egypt. In A.D. 642, after the Arabs conquered Egypt, alchemy spread to Arabia. Arabian chemists developed a theory that different metals could be made by combining various amounts of sulfur and mercury. For centuries, this theory was accepted in many other countries.

In the 1200s, Roger Bacon, a British

philosopher and alchemist, laid down the groundwork for chemical research. Unlike the earlier alchemists, Bacon carefully studied his laboratory work.

The 1500s During the 1500s, alchemists and physicians began to use their knowledge of chemistry toward the treatment of disease. Though drugs had been made and used for centuries, people did not understand how the drugs worked. The medical chemistry of this period is called iatrochemistry. Iatrochemists were the first to study chemical effects on the body. They did not fully understand how their medicines worked. Their work, however, did spark an interest in the chemistry of the body. As scientists began to learn more about medicine, they lost interest in many theories of alchemy.

The 1600s The birth of modern chemistry came in the 1600s. New theories were developed by several scientists. Jan Baptista van Helmont, a Belgian chemist and physician, believed that air and water were the only elements. In one experiment, he measured the growth of a tree which he fed only with water. The experiment led van Helmont to the theory that water was the basic element of all plants. Van Helmont invented the word gas. He studied the gases released by burning charcoal. He believed that food was digested by acids in the body.

Robert Boyle, an Irish chemist, is often looked upon as the last important alchemist and also the first real chemist. He accepted some of van Helmont's ideas about gases, especially the study of air. Boyle taught that theories must be supported by experiments. By his experiments, he proved that air, earth, fire, and water were not elements. His book, *The Skeptical Chymist*, did much to mark the final break between alchemy and chemistry.

The 1700s During this period, many elements, such as chlorine, cobalt, and man-

ganese were discovered. The study of gases led to the discovery of oxygen. The role of oxygen in chemical reactions became the key to modern chemistry.

The early gas experiments of the 1700s were based on the theories of Georg Stahl, a German chemist. Stahl believed that a substance called phlogiston escaped when a material burned. The noted chemists Karl Scheele, Joseph Priestley, and Henry Cavendish accepted the phlogiston theory. Scheele, a Swedish chemist, thought that the heat produced by chemical reactions was made up of two substances. One was phlogiston. The other was fire air. Fire air was actually oxygen. Priestley, a British chemist, also produced oxygen, calling it dephlogisticated air, meaning ''air without phlogiston.''

Antoine Lavoisier, a French chemist, offered a theory that opposed the theories proposed by Scheele, Priestley, and Cavendish. Lavoisier did not believe that phlogiston was released when a material burned. He believed that the material combined with a substance already present in the air. (*See* COMBUSTION.) Lavoisier called the substance oxygen. He showed that oxygen combined with metals to form compounds. By 1800, Lavoisier's theories were widely accepted.

The 1800s During this era, chemists discovered about half of the more than 100 known elements. Sir Humphry Davy, a British chemist, discovered sodium and potassium by electrolysis. He developed a new theory which explained the effects of electric current on chemical compounds.

Chemistry began to be broken down into different branches. There were three main branches. One was inorganic chemistry, the study of compounds that do not contain carbon. Another was organic chemistry, the study of compounds that contain carbon. A third branch, physical chemistry, was the study of heat, electricity, and other forms of energy.

In 1808, John Dalton, a British chemist, published his theory about atoms. Dalton stated that elements are made up of atoms. These atoms simply combine to form compounds. This was an important step forward in understanding chemical reactions. It was still very difficult to assign correct formulas to compounds. (*See* CHEMICAL FORMULAS AND EQUATIONS.)

By 1826, Jöns Berzelius, a Swedish chemist, made up a table of atomic weights that was fairly accurate. He also explained what catalysts and isomers were. Berzelius and other chemists could not agree on various results in figuring out atomic weights. They could not prove which results were correct.

In 1860, Cannizzaro, an Italian chemist, brought out the work of an earlier chemist, Avogadro. In 1811, Avogadro suggested that equal volumes of gases at the same temperature and pressure contain an equal number of molecules. Cannizzaro showed how Avogadro's theory could be used in measuring atomic weights. The theory proved the accuracy of the weights measured by Berzelius. Correct tables of atomic weights and molecular weights could now be drawn up. In 1869, Dmitri Mendeleev, a Russian chemist, introduced the first periodic table of the elements by arranging, according to atomic weight, all the elements known then. (*See* ELEMENT.)

Physical chemistry rapidly advanced in the 1800s. Thomas Graham, a Scottish chemist, proposed a law which came to be known as Graham's law of diffusion. This law explains how two gases mix with one another. He also did work with colloids, which are tiny particles of one substance spread evenly throughout another substance.

In the 1870s, Josiah Willard Gibbs, an American physicist, developed the phase rule, which concerns the coexistence of phases, or temporary forms, of matter. The three phases are solid, liquid, and gas. For example, water, which is normally a liquid, can be made to form steam, which is a gas.

Water can also be partly frozen to form an ice-water mixture. Later on, Wilhelm Ostwald, a German chemist, suggested the theory of ions. (*See* ELECTROCHEMISTRY.)

Chemical industry began to develop during the 1800s. New artificial drugs, fertilizers, and dyes were manufactured. Germany led the world in the chemical industry. The development there of synthetic rubber in the 1900s was the beginning of the enormous industry of manufacturing plastics.

This is the computer room at the pharmaceutical company. The technician in the foreground is checking the fermentation process in the production of antibiotics.

The 1900s In 1911, Ernest Rutherford, a British physicist, proposed a new theory of atomic structure. Rutherford thought that the atom had a nucleus with a positive electric charge. This nucleus was surrounded by electrons carrying a negative electric charge. Other physicists developed this idea further, discovering protons and neutrons.

In 1916, Gilbert N. Lewis, an American

chemist, explained the action of electrons in chemical bonds, which are forces that hold atoms together. In 1934, Frédéric and Irène Joliot-Curie discovered that artificial radioactivity could be produced. This was done by bombarding various elements with alpha particles. (*See* CURIE FAMILY.) In the 1930s, scientists knew how to produce energy by splitting the nucleus of the uranium atom. After 1940, chemists and physicists were able to produce new artificial elements by nuclear reactions. A dozen new elements have been found this way. Glenn T. Seaborg has been one of the leading United States scientists in this field. (*See* ISOTOPE, TRANSURANIUM ELEMENT.)

During the 1960s, scientists took major steps in biochemistry. Biochemists have learned how chemicals such as DNA and RNA affect heredity.

During recent years, chemists in the United States have developed special devices for exploring space. Many of these devices were designed to analyze the soil on the moon. Others were designed to look for chemical signs of life on different planets, especially Mars. (*See* SPACE TRAVEL.) J.J.A./J.M.

Most cherries are red. Some are black or flesh-colored. The main types of cherries are the sweet cherry and the sour cherry. The sweet cherry's flowers cannot pollinate others on the same tree. The sour cherry's flowers can fertilize flowers on the same tree.

CHERRY (cher′ ē) The cherry is a tree that produces small, round fruit about the size of a marble. The fruit has a single stony pit, and is related to the plum, peach, and apricot. There are many varieties of cherries, but the ones we usually grow in our gardens and orchards are the sour red cherries or the sweet black ones.

The sour cherry trees are cultivated mostly in the eastern part of the United States. The fruit is used for making pies, puddings, and other types of food. The sweet cherries grown in the United States come from the Pacific Northwest. Both kinds can be easily preserved and shipped.

In North America, the wild black cherry tree grows in southern Canada and in the northern, western, and southern regions of the United States. It is the main lumber tree of the cherry family, growing from 9 to 18 m (30 to 60 ft) in height. The fine-grained wood is used for making furniture. Some tonics are made from its bark and roots.

The flowering Japanese cherry trees are popular ornamentals. Species have been cultivated for their white and pink flowers. In 1912, the mayor of Tokyo, Japan, presented 3,000 of these trees to the United States. They were planted around the Tidal Basin and in Potomac Park, in Washington, where they are visited by many tourists each year during their time of blooming. P.G.C./M.H.S.

CHESTNUT (ches′ nət) The chestnut is a tree that belongs to the family Fagaceae. It bears a nut of the same name. There are two well-known chestnuts: the American chestnut and the Chinese chestnut.

The American chestnut was once one of the most abundant and one of the largest trees in the eastern United States. It was a valuable tree. The wood was used for building, telephone poles, railroad ties, and charcoal. The nuts are delicious and eaten by people and wildlife. In 1910, a disease was brought to New York City on Chinese chestnuts imported from China. The disease, the chestnut blight, killed almost every American chestnut within five years. The Chinese chestnut was not as seriously affected by the disease.

Chestnut trees are able to grow new sprouts from their roots. Trees that have been dead nearly seventy years still grow shoots. When the shoots get old enough to form bark, the blight kills them. Scientists are working on a cure for the blight so that the chestnut can be saved from extinction.   S.R.G./M.H.S.

Sweet chestnuts are an edible kind of chestnut.

CHICKEN POX (chik′ ən päks′) Chicken pox is a common disease usually caught by children between the ages of two and six. Adults rarely are infected.

Chicken pox is caused by a virus, an organism that is so small that it cannot be seen under an ordinary microscope. The disease can spread easily because the virus can be carried by moisture in the air. The virus is one of a group that causes the blisters known as herpes. In older adults, it may reappear as a painful skin disease called shingles.

From one to three weeks after a child has been around other children with chicken pox, small red spots may show up on his skin. These spots look like blisters and are filled with a clear fluid. At this time, the disease can be spread most easily because the virus particles are in the fluid. If the child scratches the blister or breaks it accidentally, he can release the virus and infect other children.

The child is usually not very sick. He may have a fever with a temperature rarely above 38.9°C [102°F]. Sometimes he may be tired and lose his appetite.

Chicken pox does not last very long. After four or five days, the blisters dry up and small scabs are formed. These scabs should not be scratched or they may become infected.

A person seldom has chicken pox more than once. Because the disease is so mild, doctors make no effort to prevent children from catching it.   P.G.C./J.J.F.

CHICKWEED (chik′ wēd′) Chickweed is the name given to any of several species of annual or perennial weeds belonging to the pink family. It is found throughout North America, Europe, and Asia. Chickweed grows close to the ground and has weak, branched stems with small, oval leaves. The small white flowers bloom year-round in mild climates, and may even bloom under the snow in cooler regions.

Chickweed spreads quickly and often invades lawns and field. Many generations of chickweed may be produced in a single season. (*See* EPHEMERAL PLANT.) Chickweed seeds become sticky when wet and are often carried on the fur of animals or the feathers of birds. (*See* DISPERSION OF PLANTS.) Chickweed is also called starwort, tongue grass, and winterweed.   A.J.C./M.H.S.

CHICORY (chik′ rē) Chicory (*Cichorium intybus*) is a small, biennial plant of the composite family. It grows wild throughout North America, Europe, and Asia and is cultivated in the United States and southern Canada. The chicory plant has many branches growing from a stiff, hairy stem which grows to be 1 to 1.5 m [3.3 to 5 ft] long. The leaves, which are 4 cm [1.6 in] in diameter, are lobed and look like those of the dandelion plant. Although the flowers may be white or pink, they are usually bright blue and made up of ray florets. There are relatively few of these small flowers on each plant.

The tap root is long and filled with stored food. (*See* ROOT.) It is often dried, ground, and mixed with coffee to produce a beverage that is darker and richer than coffee. Some people prefer to use pure chicory root as a substitute for coffee. When coffee prices began to rise sharply in the mid-1970s, several manufacturers released new products which were a mixture of coffee and chicory.

In addition to the roots, many people eat blanched leaves in salad. The leaves blanch, or turn white, if the plant is grown in darkness. Many farmers grow chicory as a pasture food for cattle. Chicory is sometimes called succory.   A.J.C./F.W.S.

The roots of the chicory plant are often used to make a kind of coffee.

CHIMPANZEE (chim′ pan′ zē′) The chimpanzee (*Pan troglodytes*) is the African ape with a body and a brain most like those of human beings. It is the most widespread of the anthropoids and the one that has received the most medical and psychological study. A male chimpanzee may grow to be 1.7 m [5.6 ft] tall and weigh 80 kg [176 lb]. The female is usually shorter and lighter. Chimpanzees have long, dark brown or black hair, large ears, long hands, and, like all apes, no tails. Their feet have thumblike big toes which aid in climbing trees.

The chimpanzee rarely stands upright. It spends most of its time in trees where it makes a new nest every night. Chimpanzees live in a family group with one male, several females, and the young. Chimpanzees communicate with each other by means of vocal sounds and body gestures. Their faces show a range of emotions. Chimpanzees show their affection by kissing and hugging or by gently touching each other's bodies. They are rarely aggressive. Adults spend at least an hour a day grooming each other. Chimpanzees look for food during the day and sleep at night. Although they usually eat fruits and plants, they also eat insects and small animals.

Chimpanzees mate in the fall. The female starts mating when she is 11 or 12 years old. After an eight-month pregnancy, the mother gives birth to one young. Twins are rare. She raises the baby alone until it is old enough to fend for itself (6 to 7 years). Chimpanzees live to be 40 years old. Chimpanzees in captivity live 10 to 15 years longer.

Chimpanzees are the most intelligent apes. Their brain size and structure are similar to those of human beings. Chimpanzees can imitate behavior and have been taught to dress, tie shoes, smoke cigarettes, and perform simple tricks. More importantly, though, chimpanzees show an ability to solve problems. They will make tools to help solve these problems. They have been observed putting sticks together or stacking boxes to reach food. They have a good memory and will remember people or tricks for years. Because of their behavior and physical structure, they have been used in many experiments.

In the mid-1900s, scientists tried to teach chimpanzees to speak English. Unfortunately, chimpanzees do not have the proper vocal structures to make human sounds, and the experiment failed. In the 1970s, however, several chimpanzees were taught sign language. One chimpanzee even invented new words such as "water bird" for duck. *See also* COMMUNICATION; INTELLIGENCE; PSYCHOLOGY.   A.J.C./J.J.M.

The young chimpanzee (facing left) is eating an apple.

CHINCHILLA (chin chil' ə) The chinchilla is a rodent native to the Andes Mountains of South America. It grows to about 30 cm [12 in] long and weighs 500 to 800 g [18 to 28 oz]. Related to the guinea pig, the chinchilla has long hind legs and a bushy tail about half as long as its body. The chinchilla sleeps in its burrow during the day, and comes out at night to feed on roots and grasses. Chinchillas are hunted for their thick, blue gray furs which are used to make fur coats. They are also raised on farms, or chinchilla ranches, for their fur. The first chinchillas were brought to California from Chile in 1923. Today, there are about 3,000 chinchilla farms in the United States and Canada.   G.M.B./J.J.M.

The chinchilla is a South American rodent that is hunted for its valuable fur.

CHINESE CIVILIZATION (chī nēz' siv' ə lə zā' shən) Some early forms of human beings lived in China before records of Chinese civilization began. Peking man is the name for an early form of humans who lived there about 375,000 years ago. Many scientists believe Peking man was an ancestor of a number of Asian peoples, including the Chinese.

Among the earliest records of Chinese history are those scratched on bones and stones. This form of writing used simple drawings to represent words. It became the basis of the written Chinese language and of the decorative art of calligraphy. (*See* PRINTING.) Preserved Chinese writings date from about 1500 B.C.

During this period, the Great Wall of China was begun. It was built mostly during the third century A.D. The wall is still standing, and is considered one of the greatest engineering feats in history. Built to keep out invaders from the north, it winds across some 2,415 km [1,500 mi] of rugged mountains.

Throughout the many centuries of their history, the Chinese have put great emphasis on the development of their cultural activities. Their poetry, literature, painting, architecture, music, and art have become known throughout the world. By A.D. 25, art, education, and science thrived. Chinese scholars visited much of the civilized world. They brought back histories, dictionaries, and classical literature from other lands. Chinese cities became cultural centers of the world. Many scholars and scientists came to them to study.

Although Chinese culture was admired by the world, the Chinese had not placed as much emphasis on the development of science and technology as they had on the traditional and ancient art forms.

The Chinese were able to combine art and technology to a certain extent, but this was not one of their main interests. They developed certain principles of building design that are still used by architects. In addition, Chinese architects were the first belonging to a great civilization to design buildings to fit into natural settings. At the beginning of the twentieth century this idea was used by Frank Lloyd Wright, a famous American architect.

In spite of China's relatively slow progress in science and technology, they were able to make many significant discoveries, like gunpowder, paper, the magnetic compass, and movable type for printing.

China went through various periods of

political troubles and became slightly out of touch with the rest of the world. Then it emerged, during the twentieth century, under Chiang Kai-shek and then under a Communist government. In 1953, the government began a five-year plan to increase agricultural production and to build up its industries. At the end of the first five-year plan, almost all agriculture and industry were under government control.

China has ranked among the world's leading agricultural nations for more than 4,000 years. Today it is third, after the Soviet Union and the United States. Because of its climate and geography, only about one-tenth of the land can be farmed, and one-fifth grazed. But improvements in soil conservation, terracing of slopes, and irrigation have helped agriculture. The important crops are rice, wheat, other grains, cotton, oranges, and other fruits. Livestock is used mostly for working the farms. Hogs provide an important meat for food. Sheep yield both food and wool. The fishing industry is very large.

China now ranks as one of the world's largest producers of iron and steel. China's textile industry produces cotton and wool, with silk being the most important. The most important minerals include iron ore and coal. The country is the largest coal producer after Russia and the United States.

Until recent years, transportation was provided mainly by animals and people. Now, however, motor vehicles are becoming increasingly common. Railroads link major manufacturing cities. Inland waterways, like canals and rivers, are used by boats and barges.

All forms of communication are under the control of the government. The government operates about 150 radio stations and about 40 television stations. Few Chinese, however, can afford radio and television sets. People hear and see broadcasts in public gathering places.

Real progress in science and technology began in the 1960s, when China succeeded in building its own nuclear weapons and the rockets to deliver them. In the present decade, Chinese scientists are making notable advances in laser technology and in the technology of launching space satellites.   P.G.C./S.O.

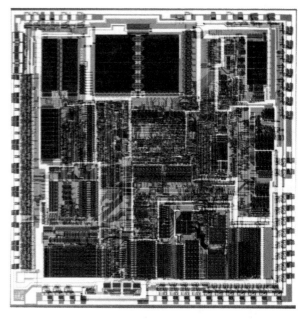

This silicon chip is a microprocessor for a large computer. The chip measures one-third of an inch on a side. It incorporates 128,000 transistors.

CHIP A chip (chip′) is a small piece or wafer of silicon. A chip can hold the electronic circuits of a computer's entire central processing unit.

Early digital computers used vacuum tubes as on-off switches. The tubes controlled the flow of electrons used to process information in the central processing unit (CPU). To perform different computer operations, the tubes had to be physically rewired like an old wire-and-plug telephone switchboard. Rewiring could take several days. In 1947 Bell Labs invented a small "sandwich" of semiconducting materials (mostly crystals of germanium) called a transistor. Later, silicon crystals were used to cause a very small current entering one part of the transistor to control a larger current in another part of it. Transistors replaced vacuum tubes for switching operations in computers because they were smaller, worked faster, and had fewer failures.

The first computers built with transistors were made like early radios, with a tangle of wires connecting the different components. Soon electronics manufacturers began "printing" the circuit wiring directly onto a board. The transistor and the miniaturized, board-printed circuit made it possible to reduce the size of a computer significantly. In the 1950s, researchers found that any number of transistors (along with the connections between them) could be etched onto one chip the size of a pea. These were called microchips, and they contained the integrated circuits for operating different parts of a computer.

Then, in 1971, a major breakthrough occurred. A microprocessor was designed that could be contained on one chip; it acted as the entire CPU of a basic computer. The chip could be programmed to do any number of tasks, from running watches to steering spacecraft.

A microprocessor chip is a complex, large-scale, integrated circuit that contains the equivalent of about 10,000 components. It controls the functions of a computer's CPU. These functions include memory for storing information until needed, a control unit which gives instructions for processing data, and the arithmetic logic unit (ALU) that performs operations as directed.

The development of microprocessors has made it possible for computer manufacturers to produce table-top, personal computers and even inexpensive, pocket-sized microcomputers and portable terminals. The low cost of these computers has led to their increased use in business and at home.

Improved chips continue to increase in capacity. They have expanded the power of computer CPUs and the complexity of computer operations. They have also been used in other electronic equipment. Increasing capacities and functions along with decreasing equipment sizes have typified the effect that chips have had on the electronics industry. *See also* COMPUTER; INTEGRATED CIRCUIT; MICROCOMPUTER.   S.K.L./G.D.B.

The chipmunk is a small relative of the squirrel.

CHIPMUNK (chip′ məngk′) The chipmunk is a small, reddish brown rodent with black and white stripes on its face, back, and sides. Belonging to the family Sciuridae, it is a close relative of the squirrel and the woodchuck. The chipmunk has strong hind legs. Although it sometimes climbs trees, the chipmunk spends most of its time in its burrow or on the ground in search of food. It feeds mainly on nuts and fruits and stores its food in its burrow. The chipmunk sleeps through much of the winter. It is native to Asia and North America. There are more than a dozen species of chipmunks found in the United States, all of which are about 20 cm [8 in] long.

G.M.B./J.J.M.

CHITIN (kīt′ ən) Chitin is the stiff, horny material that forms most of the exoskeleton, or outer covering of an animal such as an arthropod. The molecules of chitin contain nitrogen, carbon, hydrogen, and oxygen. These molecules are arranged in long chains, which are grouped into fibers. Chitin is secreted by underlying cells in the body of the animal. It is often combined with chalky materials which increase its toughness. In most crustaceans, the chitin becomes impregnated with calcium carbonate. The shells of crabs and lobsters are thick and strong. Other animals, like flies and moths, have thin, weak shells made of chitin. With the exception of its nitrogen content, chitin is similar to the cellulose of plant cells.   G.M.B./E.R.L.

Chitin is the stiff material that forms the outer covering of many animals such as arthropods. This beetle's "shell" is made of chitin.

CHITON (kīt′ ən) The chiton is a mollusk of the class Amphineura. Its shell is often brightly colored and consists of eight overlapping plates. With a muscular foot like.that of the snail or the limpet, the chiton holds onto rocks of the seacoast. It feeds on algae, which it scrapes from the surface of rocks. Although chitons are found along various rocky coasts of North America, they are most abundant and varied on the shores of California. Most chitons are 2.5 to 5 cm [1 to 2 in] long, but a large species of the Pacific coast grows to a length of 30.5 cm [12 in].   G.M.B./C.S.H.

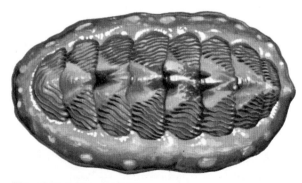

The chiton is a mollusk.

CHLORATE (klōr′ āt′) A chlorate is a compound of metals with chlorine and oxygen. The chlorine and oxygen form the chlorate radical. It is called a radical because it is almost always found combined with something else. Usually it is combined with a metal. Chlorates are dangerous chemicals. If they are mixed with something that burns easily, they can cause an explosion. This is because chlorates contain so much oxygen. Potassium chlorate is used to make explosives, matches, and fireworks. Sodium chlorate is used as a weedkiller.   M.E./A.D.

CHLORDANE (klōr′ dān′) Chlordane is a chemical compound containing chlorine, carbon, and hydrogen. It is a colorless liquid that does not dissolve in water. Chlordane is used to kill cockroaches, termites, and outdoor insect pests. Most uses of chlordane have been banned by the United States government because it may cause cancer.

J.M.C./J.M.

CHLORATE (klōr′ āt′) A chlorate is a compound of metals with chlorine and oxygen. An atom of chlorine combines with three of oxygen to form the chlorate radical. A radical is an ionized, or electrically charged, group that reacts with other elements to form compounds. Chlorates are dangerous chemicals. If they are mixed with something that burns easily, they can cause an explosion. This is because chlorates contain so much oxygen. Potassium chlorate is used to make explosives, matches, and fireworks. Sodium chlorate is used as a weedkiller.   M.E./A.D.

CHLORINE (klōr′ ēn′) Chlorine (Cl) is a poisonous, yellow green gas with a strong, choking odor. Chlorine belongs to the halogen family of chemical elements. Its atomic number is 17. It has an atomic weight of 35.45. Chlorine melts at $-100.98°C$ [$-149.7°F$] and boils at $-34.6°C$ [$-30.2°F$].

In 1774, Karl Scheele, a Swedish chemist, discovered chlorine by treating hydrochloric acid with manganese dioxide. In 1810, Sir Humphry Davy, a British chemist, showed that chlorine was an element.

Chlorine is found in nature with other elements. The most common chlorine compound, sodium chlorine (ordinary table salt), is found in oceans, salt lakes, and in rock salt. Chlorine is manufactured by passing an electric current through a water solution of sodium chloride. (*See* ELECTROLYSIS.)

Chlorine is a bleach and is present in bleaching powders and fluids. Chlorine is often used to purify water. It is also used to kill bacteria in waste material and to make insect and weed killers. Chlorine is used to process certain foods. It is also used in the manufacture of drugs, dyes, metals, and plastics. Chlorine has been used to produce various types of industrial chemicals, such as fluorocarbons, which are cooling agents used in some refrigerators.

One of the most useful chlorine compounds is hydrochloric acid, which is used in dyeing processes and in cleaning metal. Another compound, chloroform, is a solvent and an anesthetic. Chlorine is used in manufacturing chlorinated compounds that find use in pulp bleaching and textile processing. Polyvinyl chloride, or PVC, is a well-known plastic. *See also* CHLORATE; CHLORIDE.

J.J.A./J.R.W.

Chlorine is made by passing an electric current through a sodium chloride (brine) solution.

CHLOROFORM (klōr′ ə fòrm′) Chloroform (CHCl$_3$) is a colorless liquid with a strong, sweet smell. Chemically known as trichloromethane, chloroform freezes at −63.5°C [−82.3°F] and boils at 61.2°C [141.8°F].

Chloroform is used in the manufacture of fluorocarbons. (*See* CHLORINE.) Chloroform is also used as an industrial solvent, such as in the manufacture of antibiotics, dyes, and pesticides. Because chloroform has anesthetic properties, it was once commonly used to deaden pain. Other anesthetics have now replaced chloroform. When used as an anesthetic, chloroform was found to have harmful effects on the heart, liver, and kidneys.

In 1976, the United States Food and Drug Administration, commonly called the FDA, banned the use of chloroform in drugs and cosmetics. The FDA did this because tests showed that the compound could cause cancer in laboratory animals.   J.J.A./J.M.

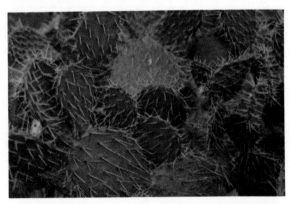

Chlorophyll is the green pigment found in most plants. In these cactuses it occurs in the stem.

CHLOROPHYLL (klōr′ ə fil′) Chlorophyll is a green pigment found in most higher plants, algae, and some bacteria. In higher plants, it is usually concentrated in the cells of the leaves. Chlorophyll is needed so the plant can make food by photosynthesis. (*See* PHOTOSYNTHESIS.) Chlorophyll is contained in small, flattened bodies called chloroplasts. Certain plant cells may contain from one to several hundred chloroplasts.

Chlorophyll contains the chemical elements carbon, hydrogen, oxygen, nitrogen, and magnesium. There are several forms of chlorophyll, the most common of which are chlorophyll a and chlorophyll b.

If a plant is kept out of the light, much of the chlorophyll breaks down. The leaves turn from green to yellow and photosynthesis stops. If the plant is kept in the dark for several weeks, it will die, having starved to death. *See also* CHLOROSIS; PLANT KINGDOM.

A.J.C./E.R.L.

CHLOROSIS (klə rō' səs) Chlorosis is a plant sickness in which the leaves become yellow due to the loss of chlorophyll. It usually happens because one of the elements needed to form chlorophyll is not available. Since carbon, hydrogen, and oxygen are all supplied by the air, the deficiency is usually in nitrogen or magnesium. If there is too little nitrogen, the leaves are small and yellow. If there is a deficiency of magnesium, the leaves are normal size, but they are yellow in the centers. These elements are replaced, and chlorosis cured, by the use of the proper fertilizers.

The term chlorosis is also used to describe a certain kind of iron-deficiency anemia that occurs in some teenage girls. It is also called greensickness because it causes the skin to turn a light green yellow color. It can be treated with iron supplements in the diet.

A.J.C./M.H.S.

CHOLERA (käl' ə rə) Cholera is a very contagious intestinal disease which, if untreated, results in dehydration, shock, and death. It is caused by a bacterium, *vibrio cholerae,* which settles in the intestines and causes severe diarrhea and vomiting. The bacteria are spread by contaminated food and water, by contact with an infected person, or by flies and other insects. Cholera is common in India and other Asian countries where there are unsanitary conditions. Every year, chol-

era kills more than 5,000 people in India. (*See* EPIDEMIC.)

Cholera symptoms last from two to seven days. Antibiotics can reduce the severity of the disease by helping the body's natural defenses. (*See* ANTIBODY.) The patient must receive intravenous feedings to replace lost body fluids, or he will become dehydrated and go into shock. There is a cholera vaccine that produces short-term immunity against the disease. *See also* CHEMICAL AND BIOLOGICAL WARFARE.

A.J.C./J.J.F.

CHOLESTEROL (kə les' tə rôl') Cholesterol is a fatty substance made in the bodies of animals and human beings. It is found in the blood, tissues, and organs, particularly the brain, liver, and arteries. Deposits of fat and cholesterol may form on the walls of the arteries, causing them to harden and to allow less blood to flow. This condition is called arteriosclerosis. Small blood clots that would normally pass through blood vessels may be trapped by these cholesterol deposits. If this occurs in a coronary artery, the result is a heart attack. (*See* HEART.)

Cholesterol is used by the body to produce several hormones, including the sex hormones. It is also used to produce bile salts used in digestion. (*See* LIVER.) Deposits of hardened cholesterol in the bile, however, may settle in the gall bladder as gall stones.

Although most medical experts feel that a certain amount of cholesterol in the diet is important, too much can be dangerous. Butter, eggs, fatty meat, liver, and brains are the main sources of cholesterol.

A.J.C./J.J.F.

CHORDATA (kòr däd' ə) Chordata is a phylum of the animal kingdom. It includes the tunicates, lancelets, and vertebrates. (*See* SEA SQUIRT.) All chordates have three features sometime during their lives: a notochord, a dorsal hollow nerve cord, and gill slits. These features are present only in the embryo of some chordates. Humans are chordates, but

The sea squirt is a member of Chordata. It is related to vertebrates because the young stages of the sea squirt have a notochord.

the gill slits and notochord disappear before they are born. Gill slits develop into gills in fishes. Tunicates and lancelets are very primitive chordates. Scientists did not realize that they were chordates until the larvae of these animals were found. The larvae have all three features of the chordates, even though the adults do not. (*See* LARVA.) *See also* CLASSIFICATION OF LIVING ORGANISMS. S.R.G./R.J.B.

CHROMATOGRAPHY (krō′ mə täg′ rə fē) Chromatography is a way of separating and identifying the various substances in a mixture. This method may be done in several ways.

Paper chromatography, sometimes called adsorption chromatography, is based on the fact that porous paper adsorbs different substances to different extremes. (*See* ABSORPTION AND ADSORPTION.) The mixture to be

studied is first dissolved in a liquid. A small drop of the solution is then placed about 1 cm [.4 in] from the edge of a strip of paper, such as filter paper. After the solution dries, the paper, with the sample spot at the bottom, is hung vertically in a glass vessel. In this position, the lower edge of the paper strip makes contact with a layer of solvent in the vessel. The solvent rises among the fibers of the paper by capillary action. In doing this, the solvent carries the various substances in the sample spot to different heights on the paper strip, thereby separating the substances. Substances which were strongly adsorbed by the paper, and mix only slightly in the solvent, rise a short distance. Substances that were not strongly adsorbed by the paper, and dissolve easily in the solvent, are carried to higher levels. If the substances in the original mixture were colored, a group of colored spots can be seen between the position of the sample spot and the top of the paper strip. Each spot contains one of the substances in the original mixture. The paper strip is now called

solvent

A paper chromatogram, right, is used to separate the parts of a mixture. The mixture is carried up the paper by a solvent which is itself "pulled" upward by capillary action with the paper fibers. Some parts of the mixture are carried up quicker than others, causing them to separate into colored bands.

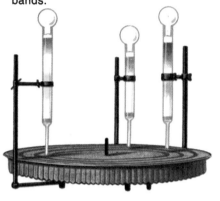

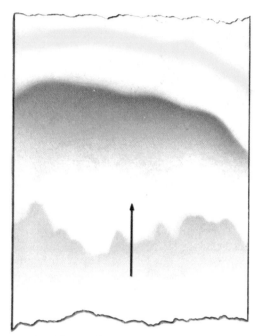

Above left, mixtures are separated in a solvent contained in a column chromatograph. Above, column chromatographs are held on a turntable.

Below, a gas chromatograph. In this instrument, the mixture to be analyzed is carried in the form of a vapor by a carrier gas. As in the examples above, some parts of the mixture will be carried more quickly than others, separating the mixture into its parts. The carrier gas is burned at the outlet of the chromatograph. The heat of the flame will vary for each carried part. This heat variation is measured and recorded as shown below.

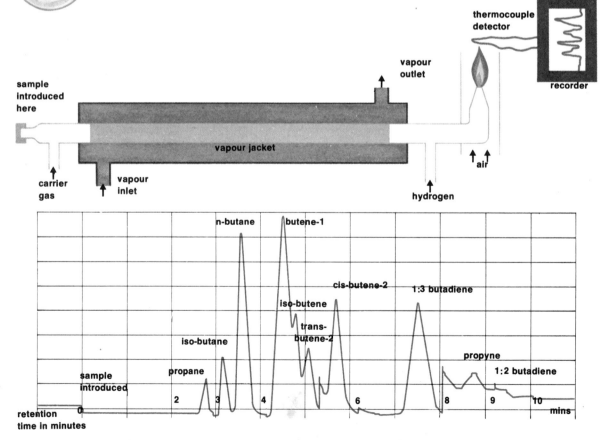

a chromatogram. It is removed from the glass vessel and dried. Certain substances can often be identified by the heights they reach on the chromatogram. To be accurate, it is necessary to perform the chromatography under certain strict conditions. This means using a standard type of paper and solvents. The substances in each spot can be removed from the paper by treatment with a certain solvent. This process is called elution. Once a solution of the purified substance has been obtained, it can be identified by chemical tests.

Chromatography can also be used to separate and identify mixtures of colorless substances. In order to do this, the chromatogram is sprayed with certain chemicals. The chemicals react with the substances to be studied, producing colored compounds.

Thin-layer chromatography is almost the same process as paper chromatography. In thin-layer chromatography, the paper is replaced by a sheet of glass on which a thin layer of absorbent–such as silica gel—has been placed.

In adsorption chromatography, as described before, the adsorbent material, such as the paper, is often called the stationary phase. The solvent is called the moving phase. In partition chromatography, both the moving phase and the stationary phase are liquid. The stationary phase is often held by a sheet of solid material, such as a paper strip or silica gel. The moving phase passes up or down on the solid material. The distance moved by a certain substance in the sample spot depends on the difference in solubilities of the substance in each of the two liquid phases.

Gas chromatography is a type of partition chromatography. The stationary phase is a liquid. The moving phase is a gas. Gas chromatography is often used to study substances that form vapors. Chemists use gas chromatography to find out what chemical compounds are present in mixtures such as petroleum products, smog, cigarette smoke, and coffee aroma. *See also* CHEMICAL ANALYSIS; SOLUTION AND SOLUBILITY.

J.J.A./A.D.

chromite crystals

chromite

Chromium is a widely used metal. It is plated on other metals to protect them, and is used on many everyday objects. It is a hard metal and does not lose its shine through corrosion. It is used with nickel to make some stainless steels. Chromite, a brownish-black mineral, is the main ore of the metal chromium.

CHROMIUM (krō' mē əm) Chromium (Cr) is a hard, brittle, gray metal. It has an atomic number of 24. Its atomic weight is 51.99. Chromium melts at about 1870°C [3398°F] and boils at 2480°C [4500°F].

Chromium, sometimes called chrome, occurs only as a combined metal. It is usually found combined with iron and oxygen in a mineral called chromite. It is mined chiefly in Rhodesia, Turkey, India, the Soviet Union, Canada, Cuba, and the Phillipines.

Chromium resists corrosion. It becomes very shiny when polished. Because of these properties, chromium is widely used to coat, or plate, other metals. The metal is used to plate automobile bumpers and door handles. Chromium is also used to harden steel. Its alloys are used to make safes, ball bearings, and the cutting edges of various tools. Alloys that have more than 10% chromium are called stainless steels. Stainless steel is used to make silverware and kitchen equipment. Many chromium compounds are important in industry. Potassium dichromate is used in tanning leather. Lead chromate, also called chrome yellow, is a pigment (coloring substance) for paint. Some chromium compounds are used in the aircraft industry to anodize aluminum, or coat it with a thick, protective, oxide film.

J.J.A./J.R.W.

CHROMOPLAST (krō′ mə plast′) A chromoplast is a small object found in plant cells. It gives a yellow or orange color to the plant because it contains two pigments: carotene and xanthophyll. In some plants, chromoplasts are present in and give color to flowers, fruit, and roots. *See also* PIGMENT.

J.M.C./M.H.S.

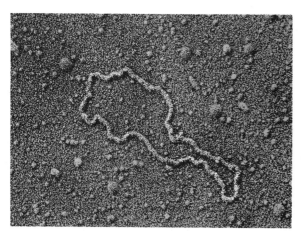

This electron microscope photo of a DNA molecule has been colored to show it more clearly.
© STANLEY N. COHEN/PHOTO RESEARCHERS, INC.

CHROMOSOME (krō′ mə sōm′) Chromosomes are small, threadlike bodies found in the nucleus of every cell. They contain chains of DNA called genes. Genes control the inherited characteristics of an organism.

Each species of plant and animal has a specific number of chromosomes. For example, human beings have 46, and cows have 60. Most organisms have chromosomes arranged in pairs. The 46 human chromosomes are actually 22 ordinary pairs plus 1 pair of sex chromosomes. There are two kinds of sex chromosomes, the X chromosome and the Y-chromosome. They are named X and Y because of the way they look under a microscope. In the cells of the human female, there are two X chromosomes. The male has one X and one Y in each cell.

Chromosomes can only be seen at certain times, and then only with a powerful microscope. Chromosomes ''appear'' in the nucleus just before a cell splits into two daughter cells. In mitosis, each chromosome splits lengthwise into two chromosomes, one for each daughter cell. In meiosis, the chromosomes do not split, so each daughter cell has only half the regular number of chromosomes. These cells develop into germ cells—sperm or egg. The egg produced by a human female has an X chromosome and 22 regular chromosomes. The sperm produced by a human male has either an X or a Y chromosome, plus 22 regular chromosomes. When an egg and a sperm combine to form a zygote, it has 44 regular chromosomes, and 2 sex chromosomes, or 46 in all. (*See* REPRODUCTION.)

The relationship between chromosomes and heredity was first suggested in 1902. In 1920, the American zoologist, Thomas Morgan, published his studies showing that inherited characteristics were controlled by genes linked on chromosomes. He used the fruit fly (*Drosophila melanogaster*) because it has only four pairs of chromosomes. Morgan's research showed that in the fruit fly there were four groups of linked characteristics. In later experiments, Morgan mapped the chromosomes, finding the exact positions of specific genes responsible for specific inherited characteristics. *See also* GENETICS; HEREDITY.

A.J.C./E.R.L.

CHRONOMETER (kro näm′ ət ər) A chronometer is a portable instrument that is used to measure time. It is more accurate than an ordinary watch or clock. Chronometers are used by ships at sea and by surveyors and auto racers. The marine chronometer is the best-known type of chronometer. It is used for navigation. Navigators need accurate timepieces so that they can determine their position. The first marine chronometer was built in 1764 by John Harrison, an Englishman. It lost only five seconds on a voyage that lasted six weeks.

The time on a marine chronometer is usually preset to coincide with Greenwich Mean Time (GMT). This is the international marine standard time. A navigator uses a sextant to measure the position of the sun in the sky (*See* SEXTANT.) Then, by knowing the time in GMT, he or she can work out the longitude of the ship.

Marine chronometers are very delicate instruments. Some of them contain 1,000 parts. They are kept inside wooden boxes to protect them from dust and corrosion by the salty air. Inside the box they are specially mounted. This allows them to stay in a horizontal position no matter how the ship moves. Marine chronometers must be kept away from the magnetic influences of compasses and vibrations from engines.

The most accurate chronometer is the atomic clock. These clocks are accurate to within one second in 10,000 years. Navigators at sea can receive radio signals that give them time checks from an atomic clock on land. *See also* CLOCK AND WATCH.

M.E./R.W.L.

CHRYSANTHEMUM (kris an′ thə məm) The chrysanthemum is a flowering herbaceous plant that grows as a shrub in temperate regions of the world. It is a member of the composite family. Most of the more than 1,000 species of chrysanthemum are perennial, but some are annual. The name of this plant comes from two Greek words meaning "golden flower."

The chrysanthemum blossom is actually a group of several flowers, and it may measure 20 cm [8 in] across. Chrysanthemums bloom near the end of the year, when the days have fewer than twelve hours of sunlight. They are called short-day plants. (*See* PHOTOPERIOD.) Since florists can control the number of hours of sunlight that a plant receives, they can cause chrysanthemums to bloom at any time during the year. New plants are produced by cutting or division. (*See* VEGETATIVE PROPAGATION.)

The chrysanthemum was grown in China in 500 B.C. All the colors that have developed from the original yellow are hybrids. Chrysanthemums were brought to Europe in 1789 and have spread throughout the world. A common nickname for the chrysanthemum is mum. *See also* ANGIOSPERM; GENETICS.

A.J.C./M.H.S.

chrysanthemum

CICADA (sə kād′ ə) The cicadas are fairly large insects belonging to the family Cicadidae. The biggest of these bugs has a body length of 8 cm [3 in]. With four, usually transparent, wings, cicadas move among the plants they use for food. They suck sap from plants with their strong beaks. Most of the 1,500 species of cicadas live in the warm regions of the world. More than 100 species

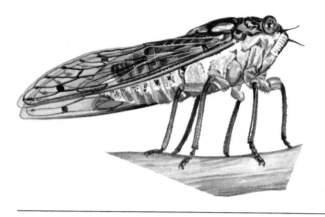

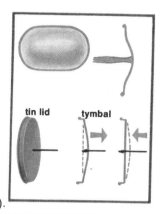

Left, a male cicada, known for its shrill "song." This song is made by rapid vibrations of two tiny membranes (tymbals) on the sides of the body. A muscle attached to the inside of the tymbal contracts and pulls the membrane inward. Each movement makes a sound like that made by denting a tin lid (left).

are found in the United States. The male cicadas make loud, shrill noises; the female cicadas are usually quiet. The sound of a cicada is produced by vibrating membranes called tymbals on the sides of its body. Although some people dislike the sounds produced by the cicadas, other people keep them in cages like singing canaries.

The life cycle of the cicadas includes long periods underground, where they prepare for a brief adult life above the ground. The 17-year cicada, a species living in the eastern United States, spends 13 to 17 years underground. The green-and-black dog-day cicada is also found in the United States. Most cicadas spend from two to five years underground.

Female cicadas lay their eggs in slits that they cut in the twigs of living trees. After about a month or so the eggs hatch and the young, called nymphs, drop to the ground. The nymphs then bury themselves deep in the soil. They live by sucking the sap from the roots of trees. They reach the surface by crawling up the roots and trunk of a tree. A short time after they have left the ground, the cicadas lose their outer skins, which split down the back. (*See* MOLTING.) Then they fly away to mate, lay eggs, and live for a few weeks. Cicadas are commonly and incorrectly called locusts.   G.M.B./J.R.

CICHLID (sik′ ləd) A cichlid is a freshwater fish that belongs to the family Cichlidae. Cichlids are found in tropical waters of South America, Africa, and southwestern Asia. There are over 200 species in the world. These colorful fish look similar to the sunfishes of North America. (*See* SUNFISH.) Some species of cichlids carry their eggs and newly hatched fish in their mouths until the small fish can protect themselves. Some cichlids are popular with sport fishermen. Others are used for food. Some are kept as aquarium fish. In the United States, a well-known fish called the oscar, which is sold in pet stores, is a cichlid.   S.R.G./E.C.M.

Some species of cichlids carry their young in their mouths when danger threatens.

CILIUM (sil′ ē əm) A cilium is a movable, hairlike structure found in cells of living things. (*See* CELL.) It can be used to move the cell. A paramecium moves itself by using many waving cilia. Cilia also move objects along the cell's surface. The windpipe in humans has cilia inside of it to move mucus and particles out of the lungs. (*See* LUNG, TRACHEA.) Cilia are similar to flagella, but they are shorter. (*See* FLAGELLUM.) *See also* PROTOZOA.   S.R.G./E.R.L.

Right, diagrams of electrical circuits. 1. A circuit powered by an electrical cell, which lights up a lamp in the circuit. The smaller diagram shows how a cell is represented by a symbol. 2. An open circuit, in which the lamp does not light up because no electricity flows, and the same circuit closed by a switch. 3. Three lamps in series, which all light up when the switch is closed. 4. Three lamps connected in parallel. When switch A is closed, only two lamps will light up. The left-hand lamp will light up only when switch is also closed.

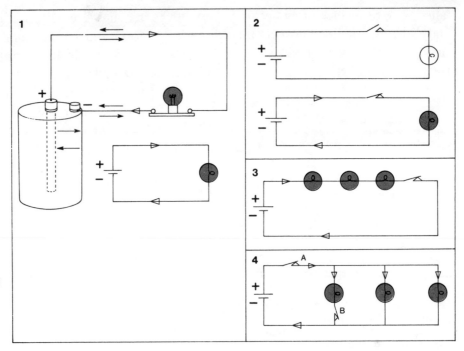

CIRCUIT, ELECTRIC An electric circuit (sər′ kət) is a path along which an electric current may flow. There are three main parts to an electric circuit. One is a source of electric energy, such as a battery or generator. Another is an output device, such as a motor, lamp, or bulb. The third is a connection between the source and the output device, such as a wire or cable. One example of a simple circuit is in a common flashlight. Electrons from the negative terminal of a battery pass through the filament of a bulb and return to the positive terminal.

Various devices can control the current flowing in an electric circuit. A switch may easily turn a light on or off. When the switch is off, a gap separates the connecting wires. The current cannot complete its path. A circuit with this type of gap is called an open circuit. A closed circuit has no gaps in the path of the current.

The word ''circuit'' may also mean a complete electrical unit or section, such as an amplifier, within a larger piece of equipment, such as a radio receiver.

There are many, very complicated types of electric circuits. But they all work in one of two main ways, or a combination of these two ways. In the flashlight circuit mentioned before, the same current passes through the bulb, battery, and the switch. The parts, or components, of this circuit, namely the bulb and switch, are said to be in series with the battery. This unit therefore has a series circuit. In any series circuit, the current passing through each component is the same.

In a parallel circuit, two or more separate circuits, or parts of a circuit, are fed by a common source of voltage. In this type of circuit, the currents passing through each individual circuit may be quite different. All household lights and appliances are connected in parallel because a parallel circuit allows all devices to operate on the same voltage. The voltage does not change if a piece of equipment is added or removed. However, the total current passing through the fuse or breaker may increase or decrease. The total current is the sum of the currents used by each piece of equipment.

A short circuit occurs when a circuit having a very low resistance is connected to a source of voltage, such as the main supply in a house. A large current flows through the resistance. The resistance often becomes very hot and sometimes melts. Short circuits can cause fires. *See also* CIRCUIT BREAKER; ELECTRICITY; FUSE, ELECTRIC.   J.J.A./J.T.

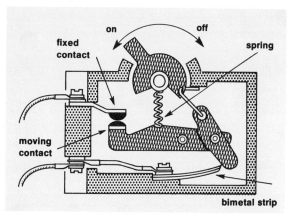

Above, a miniature circuit breaker. The bimetallic strip gets hot and bends when the current is too great. This causes the main contacts to separate and breaks the current flow.

CIRCUIT BREAKER (sər′ kət brā′ kər) A circuit breaker is an automatic switch that starts or stops the flow of an electric current. Circuit breakers are made to allow a certain amount of electric current to pass through a circuit. (*See* CIRCUIT, ELECTRIC.) The circuit breaker opens or breaks the circuit if there is too much current flowing through.

The circuit is broken or opened by the mechanical separation of contacts. Heat-sensitive devices are also used to open the switch. (*See* THERMOSTAT.) When the switch opens, an electric arc is produced. This arc is usually extinguished by an air blast or sometimes by an oil that surrounds the contacts.

Circuit breakers are used in huge electric power plants as well as in ordinary homes. They are convenient because once the problem has been corrected, the circuit breaker can be switched back on again. There is no fuse to repair or replace.   J.M.C./J.T.

CIRCULATORY SYSTEM (sər′ kyə lə tōr′ ē sis′ təm) The group of organs in animals which passes blood throughout a body is called the circulatory system. Blood must reach every cell in a body to provide it with food and oxygen and to carry away waste products. In lower animals that have only a few cells, blood and a circulatory system are not necessary. Food, oxygen, and waste products can pass freely throughout the body, reaching every cell. (*See* DIFFUSION.) This is not possible in larger animals that have millions of cells in tissue several inches thick. A circulatory system evolved to pass the blood and products to each cell. (*See* EVOLUTION.) In most animals, the system has a muscular pump, called a heart, to move the blood through long, tubelike blood vessels. Blood vessels carry the blood throughout the body to the cells.

There are two types of circulatory systems: an open system and a closed system. Members of the animal phyla Arthropoda and Mollusca have open systems. Open systems do not have blood vessels to take the blood to every cell. Blood is pumped into open spaces called sinuses. The blood bathes the cells surrounding each sinus. Some members of Mollusca and Annelida and all vertebrates have a closed system in which blood remains in blood vessels.

In a closed circulatory system, there are four types of blood vessels: arteries, arterioles, capillaries, and veins. An artery is a large vessel that carries blood away from the heart to the cells. It branches into the smaller arterioles which branch into very small vessels called capillaries. Capillaries carry blood to the cells. Veins carry blood away from the cells back to the heart. Scientists guess there are about 60,000 miles of blood vessels in our bodies.

Blood is pumped from the right ventricle of the heart into the pulmonary artery. The pulmonary artery carries the blood into the lungs, where it absorbs oxygen and releases carbon dioxide. (*See* LUNG.) The blood returns to the left auricle of the heart through the pulmonary vein. The left auricle pumps the oxygenated blood into the left ventricle of the heart which pumps it into the aorta. The aorta is the largest artery in the body. It carries blood to other arteries and arterioles. The blood absorbs food when it passes near the small intestines. (*See* DIGESTION.) Wastes from the cells are removed from the blood when it passes through the kidneys. (*See* EXCRETION.) After the blood passes through the cells of the body, delivering food and oxygen and removing waste, it returns to the heart through the vena cava. The vena cava is the largest vein of the body. The unoxygenated blood enters the right auricle which returns it to the right ventricle. It is then pumped to the lungs to receive more oxygen and make another trip.

The circulatory system in fish is different. The blood that receives oxygen from the gills does not return to the heart before traveling to the body. The heart of amphibians and reptiles mixes oxygenated and unoxygenated blood. *See also* APOPLEXY; ARTERIOSCLEROSIS; HUMAN BODY.　　S.R.G./J.J.F.

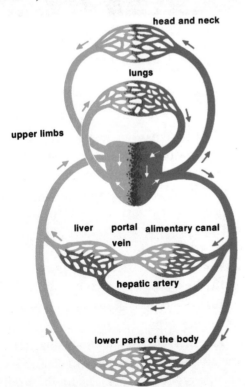

The human circulatory system: veins (blue) and arteries (red) carry blood to and from the heart.

CIRRHOSIS (sə rō′ səs) Cirrhosis is a disease which causes some of the spongy liver tissue to become scarred and useless. It can be caused by excessive use of alcohol, a poor diet, inhaling poisonous fumes, or by hepatitis, an inflammation of the liver. Once liver tissue is scarred, it cannot be repaired, and the liver may stop its work of making proteins and purifying the blood. (*See* CIRCULATORY SYSTEM.)

Cirrhosis can block the blood vessels to the liver and cause internal bleeding. Many people with cirrhosis become weak and lose weight. In some people, the abdomen swells up with excess body fluids. Sufferers of this disease may develop a yellowness of the skin and eyes called jaundice. Jaundice occurs when some of the liver fluid, bile, backs up into the blood.

Some early cases of cirrhosis can be treated by drugs, proper diet, and by avoiding alcohol. If not controlled, cirrhosis can lead to coma and death. *See also* ALCOHOLISM.
　　A.J.C./J.J.F.

CITRIC ACID (si′ trik as′ əd) Citric acid is the organic acid that gives lemons, limes, and oranges their sharp taste. It may be obtained from fruit juices or by the fermentation of molasses. In living cells, citric acid is important in chemical reactions that produce energy.　　J.M.C./J.M.

CITRUS FRUIT (si′ trəs früt′) A citrus fruit is the fruit of any of the evergreen trees and shrubs of the genus *Citrus*. The 16 species of citrus are members of the rue family. Citrus trees grow 3 to 8 m [10 to 26.5 ft] tall and have long, shiny, pointed leaves. Citrus flowers are usually white with five overlapping petals. Citrus plants thrive in warm, subtropical areas where there is little frost and wind. They are native to India and southeast Asia, and were first cultivated in China in 1000 B.C. They are now grown in many areas of the United States, such as Texas, Arizona,

Above, picking and crating ripe oranges. The orange is one of sixteen species of the genus *citrus*. Oranges live and thrive in warm, subtropical climates such as those in Florida and California. The orange can be eaten raw or squeezed for its juice. It is an important source of vitamin C in the diet.

Florida, and California. They are also grown in many areas of the world.

Citrus fruits contain seeds surrounded by a juicy, edible pulp. This pulp is divided into sections and is enclosed in a pith and colored rind. The pith and rind are usually called the "skin." The pith and rind are easily peeled to expose the pulp. Citrus fruits are a popular and tasty food. Some of them are the orange, grapefruit, lemon, lime, tangerine, shaddock, and kumquat.

Citrus fruits can be eaten raw, squeezed for their juice, or cooked in a variety of foods. They are rich in necessary vitamins and minerals. (*See* NUTRITION.) Most citrus fruits are a good source of vitamin C, a necessary part of the diet. A deficiency of vitamin C can result in fatigue and diseases such as scurvy.

A.J.C./F.W.S.

CIVET (siv′ ət) The civet is a carnivorous mammal native to the forests of Africa and southern Asia. Each of the 15 species is cat-like in appearance with a long, bushy tail and a pointed snout. Civets vary in color from black and brown to tan and gray. Most are spotted and have tails with rings of different colored fur. Some species may grow as long as 100 cm [3.3 ft] and may weigh 11 kg [24.2 lb].

Most civets live alone or in pairs in burrows in the ground. They hunt at night for birds, frogs, rodents, and other small animals. Some civets eat plants and some animal eggs. Civets are good climbers, using their tails for support.

Most species of civets have special glands

near the base of the tail. These glands produce and spray out a foul-smelling liquid which can be used to mark out a territory or to scare away an enemy. This gland is also sometimes removed and used as a base for certain kinds of musk perfumes. *See also* MONGOOSE.

A.J.C./J.J.M.

CLASS (klas) A class, in the classification of living things, is a subdivision of a phylum. It is made up of a group of related orders. *See also* CLASSIFICATION OF LIVING ORGANISMS.

A.J.C./M.H.S.

CLASSIFICATION OF LIVING ORGANISMS

Biologists try to arrange all living things (plants and animals) into a family-like group. This helps explain one organism's relationship to another organism. To do this, biologists must study all groups of organisms and compare them. This study is called taxonomy. A scientist who studies taxonomy is called a taxonomist. Taxonomists have identified more than one million types of animals and nearly a half a million plants. Each one is assigned a name and a place in the classification system. Some organisms are easy to classify. A moose, for example, is very similar to a deer and belongs to the deer family. Other organisms are hard to classify. Taxonomists cannot tell whether some one-celled organisms are plants or animals. Not all taxonomists agree with each other and some classify organisms differently. Taxonomy tries to describe nature's living creatures in a neat, clear-cut manner. Organisms are not naturally organized in a neat, clear-cut manner, so that taxonomy is never perfectly correct.

The modern method of classifying organisms was started by a Swedish naturalist named Linnaeus. All classification names are Latin, which is a common scientific language. If the names were in English, scientists in other countries would not easily understand them. By using Latin names, a Russian scientist can understand what organisms an American scientist is talking about. It is important that the name for an organism be the same all over the world. In the United States, there is a fish called a blue-gill. In the northeastern part of the country, this fish is often called a johnny roach. In the southern part of the country, this fish is often called a bream. In England, however, there is a totally different fish called a bream. This can become very confusing. Therefore, the bluegill is assigned the scientific name *Lepomis macrochirus,* regardless of where it is found.

Most scientists use a five-kingdom system of classification. Each organism belongs to one of these five kingdoms. The plant kingdom includes all multicellular plants. The animal kingdom includes all multicellular animals. The kingdom Protista includes all one-celled animals, the protozoans. The fungus kingdom includes all types of fungi. Kingdom Monera includes bacteria and blue-green algae. These kingdoms are broken down into phyla. Organisms with similar characteristics are assigned to the same phylum. All animals with a backbone belong to the phylum Chordata. Phyla are broken down into different classes. All animals with backbones that have hair and milk-producing glands are assigned to the class Mammalia. Classes are broken down into different orders. Orders are broken down into different families. Families are broken down into different genera (plural of genus). Genera are broken down into different species. Species are individual groups of identical organisms. There can be many organisms in the same genus but only one organism in each species. The scientific name (binomial nomenclature) of an organism refers to the name of its genus and species written together. Therefore, *Lepomis macrochirus* (bluegill) belongs to the genus *Lepomis* and the species *macrochirus. See also* ANIMAL KINGDOM; EVOLUTION; PLANT KINGDOM.

S.R.G./E.R.L.

Clay excavated from this pit near Blackpool in Britain is used to make English china.

CLAVICLE (klav′ i kəl) The clavicle is a bone found in mammals. It is long and slender. One end of the clavicle attaches to the breastbone, or sternum, and the other end attaches to the shoulder blade. The clavicle is also called the collarbone. Children commonly break their clavicles. *See also* BONE; SKELETON. S.R.G./J.J.F.

CLAY (klā) Clay is a soft, pliable, mineral substance found in most soil and in many rocks. It is composed of tiny, sheetlike particles of clay minerals along with quartz and other minerals. Clay minerals are similar in composition and shape to mica but are much smaller in size. Clay can be brown, red, or gray depending upon its contents. Iron oxide, for example, colors it red. Clays that contain large amounts of carbon compounds are gray.

Clay plays an important role in agricul-

In the classification of living organisms, the moose belongs to the phylum Chordata, class Mammalia and order Artiodactyla.

ture. It absorbs ammonia and other gases needed for the growth of plants. Clay also helps soil retain the fertilizing substances supplied by manure. Too much clay prevents the movement of air and water through the soil and makes the soil stiff and heavy.

There are two general types of clay, expandable clay and nonexpandable clay. Expandable clay swells up when water is added to it. It can become liquid if enough water is added. Nonexpandable clay becomes soft when water is added, but does not swell up or become liquid. Expandable clays, called bentonites, are used to make drilling mud in the petroleum industry. (*See* PETROLEUM.) Other types of expandable clays are used as chemical agents in the refining of oil. Nonexpandable clay is used in the ceramics industry to make bricks, tile, pottery, and porcelain. Molded clay objects are placed in special ovens called kilns. The intense heat removes the water from the clay and makes it hard and

KEY

Cold snow climates
(treeless)

Boreal forest and
snow climate

Temperate rainy
climate

Arid climate

Tropical rain
climate

impenetrable. It cannot be softened again by adding water.

Kaolin, or china clay, is a white clay derived mainly from decomposed feldspar that is used to make porcelain. Kaolin is also added to paper to give it whiteness, strength, and a shiny surface. Fire clay contains a large amount of silica, a material that is highly resistant to heat. Bricks made from fire clay are used to build fireplaces and to line furnaces.   W.R.P./R.H.

CLICK BEETLE (klik′ bēt′ əl) Click beetles are any of 7,000 species of the family Elateridae. They are narrow, hard insects that measure 3 to 54 mm [.12 to 2 in]. Click beetles are able to flick themselves up if they fall on their backs. The fallen beetle flips in the air with a loud click. The beetle rights itself while in the air.

The larvae of the click beetle are called wire worms. They damage crops by eating the roots in the soil.   J.M.C./J.R.

CLIMATE

Climate (klī′ mət) is the average weather experienced by an area over a period of years. It is often described in terms of temperature and precipitation. The climate of a tropical island may be described as a tropical rain climate. This means average temperatures are in the 29° to 37.5°C [85° to 100°F] range, and there are periods of rain during many days of the year.

Climate influences the type of houses we live in, the clothes we wear, the food we eat, and the types of transportation we use. We control the climate in our homes with insulation, heating, and air conditioning.

Climate and weather are not the same. Weather is the condition of the atmosphere during a given period of time. Weather changes from day to day. Scientists determine the climate of an area by studying its daily weather over several years. The study of climate is called climatology, and those who do that work are called climatologists. Climatologists consider many characteristics of the atmosphere, including temperature, precipitation, humidity, sunshine, wind, air pressure, and cloudiness. Climatologists recognize five broad bands, or zones, of climate. The zones were first suggested in 500 B.C. by Parmenides, a Greek philosopher. They include the tropical zone, the arid zone, the temperate zone, and two cold, or polar, zones. (See map on opposite page.) The tropical zone extends north and south of the equator, as does the arid zone. The temperate zone covers the middle latitudes of the north and south hemispheres. The cold zones cover the areas near the North and South Poles. There are 12 major subdivisions of climate within these zones. They are: (1) tropical wet, (2) tropical wet and dry, (3) highlands, (4) desert, (5) steppe, (6) subtropical, (7) subtropical moist, (8) oceanic moist, (9) continental moist, (10) subarctic, (11) polar, and (12) icecap.

Why climates differ Climates differ for a number of reasons, including differences in latitude, differences in land and water temperatures, and differences in the surfaces of land. Latitude is the most important factor. Areas at different distances north and south of the equator receive different amounts of heat from the sun. This is because the position of the sun in the sky varies with the latitude. In areas near the equator, the sun shines almost directly overhead at noon throughout most of the year. These direct rays of the sun produce high temperatures on the ground. Consequently, these areas have warm to hot climates.

At the North and South Poles, the sun never gets very high above the horizon. The rays of the sun are slanted and produce much less heat on the ground. Thus, these areas have cold climates. Areas in the middle latitudes between the equator and the Poles

have temperatures that average between those of the other two areas. These are the temperate climates.

Places at different distances from the equator have different amounts of precipitation. More rain falls on areas near the equator. There, warm air absorbs water easily from the warm oceans and deposits it on the land in the form of rain. On the other hand, relatively little precipitation occurs at the Poles because cold air does not absorb water easily from cold oceans.

Since most of the earth's surface is covered by water, it is apparent that water plays a major role in world climate. For example, two places within the same latitude may have different climates because one of them is adjacent to a large body of water, and the other isn't. Water heats and cools more slowly than land does. Bodies of water stay cooler than the nearby land in the summer. Cool breezes blow from the water onto the shore and help keep the shore cooler than inland areas. In the winter, the water stays warmer than the nearby land, and breezes off the water make coastal climates milder than inland climates. The New England states, for example, are in the same latitude as some of the midwestern farm belt states. Parts of the New England states tend to have milder winters and cooler summers because they border the Atlantic Ocean.

Areas that border oceans may have their climates further affected by ocean currents. The Gulf Stream is a current that brings warm water from the Caribbean Sea, through the Atlantic Ocean, to the vicinity of the British Isles. It keeps the British Isles warmer than coastal areas of Canada and Europe, which are in the same latitude.

Differences in the surface of the land account for many differences among climates. Mountains, for example, can have a major effect on the climate of nearby lowlands. As air rises to pass over a mountain, it becomes cooler and releases its moisture in the form of

Different kinds of climates. Upper left, the sand and sparse vegetation of the desert is an example of an arid climate. Upper right, a rain forest in a tropical climate. Left, Eskimos' igloos protect them from the bitter weather in polar climates. Right, the peak of Mount Kilimanjaro in East Africa is an example of a cold snow climate, even though the mountain itself is in a hot climate.

rain and snow. A place located on a mountain slope is generally cooler and wetter than a place at lower elevation. The Cascade mountain range that runs through western Oregon and Washington keeps moisture-laden air from the Pacific Ocean from reaching eastern areas of those states. Thus, those areas have dry climates. Even gentle slopes can affect climate. In the northern hemisphere, places located on gently sloping land that faces North tend to have cooler climates than places located on sloping land that faces South.

The climate of a large city is affected by many artificial objects. Tall buildings and street pavements tend to absorb heat from the sun and send it back into the lower atmosphere. Also, escaping heat from the heating systems of the buildings and hot exhaust gases of thousands of vehicles help warm the air in winter. Winter temperatures in many northern cities are often higher than those in surroundings suburban areas. City temperatures tend generally to be warmer than those in the suburbs.

The changing climate Climate changes slowly over a period of many years. A gradual worldwide cooling pattern, for example, started in the late 1940s and is still evident today. Yet the climate of North America is warmer than it was 15,000 years ago when glaciers covered Canada and the northern part of the United States. Climatologists believe the slow movement of polar ice toward the warmer areas is an effect of the climate getting colder. Climatologists have theorized that changes in the earth's orbit around the sun or changes in the sun itself have resulted in less heat from the sun's rays. Another reason given for the cooling trend is the presence of dust from volcanic eruptions in the upper atmosphere. Scientists point out that this dust can remain in the upper atmosphere for years and it may be preventing some sunlight from reaching the earth.

A factor working against worldwide cooling is called the "greenhouse effect." While the carbon dioxide in the air prevents heat from escaping from the atmosphere, it does let sunlight reach the earth. Since 1900, the level of carbon dioxide in the atmosphere has been increasing greatly because of the large amounts of fossil fuel burned in home furnaces and factories, and by automobiles. Carbon dioxide is a by-product of this burning.

Climatologists are trying to gain a better understanding of long-range climate changes so that they can predict their effects on world food production. Periods of extreme wet or dry weather, for example, can seriously affect the amount of food crops grown in the world. Advance knowledge of these changes in climate would help farmers prepare for them. *See also* ATMOSPHERE; METEOROLOGY; WEATHER.   W.R.P./C.R.

CLIMBING PLANT (klī′ ming plant′) A climbing plant relies on other plants or structures for support. It is usually very tall with a relatively weak, herbaceous stem. Many climbing plants have evolved special structures for attaching to a host. Most of these involve thigmotropism, the ability of some plants to grow in a certain direction in response to touch. (*See* TROPISM.)

Some plants, such as hops and morning glory, have stems that grow in a spiral fashion around the stems of other plants. In some plants, such as the grape and other members of the vine family, the leaf stalks or modified leaves wrap around the stem or twig or around another plant. (*See* TENDRIL.) The stem of ivy produces roots that grow into or onto walls or tree trunks. The Virginia creeper has sucker pads. Most members of the rose family have thorns for holding onto a host. Some climbing plants have no specialized structures for support, but rest on a host plant. *See also* EPIPHYTE; MOVEMENT OF PLANTS.

A.J.C./M.H.S.

CLINOMETER (klī näm′ ət ər) A clinometer is an instrument used by surveyors and civil engineers to measure the angle of inclination of slopes and hills by reference to a plumb bob, or spirit level. Clinometers can be used to measure the height of an object if the distance from the observer to the object is known.

Pocket models carried by surveyors usually consist of a flat base with a built-in spirit level, and folding metal arms, or vanes at each end. The surveyor first makes sure that the bubble is in the middle of the spirit level tube. That indicates that the clinometer is being held in a horizontal position. He or she looks through an eyehole in the rear vane, and a vertical slit in the front vane. The vertical slit is marked in degrees. The top of the hill as seen through the front slit gives the angle of inclination.

In the plumb bob type, a plumb bob, or weight attached to a piece of string, hangs from the sighting device. As the device is tilted upward to view the top of the hill, the string moves across a protractorlike face and indicates the angle of inclination. W.R.P./J.T.

CLOCK AND WATCH

A clock (kläk) is an instrument that shows the time. A watch (wäch) is a small, portable clock. A clock or watch usually has a dial or "face" on which there is a ring of evenly spaced numbers. The hands on the face of the clock or watch may point toward any of the numbers, thereby showing the time. Some clocks and watches display a changing number instead of having moving hands and stationary numbers.

History Sundials, invented more than 4,000 years ago, are the oldest known instruments designed to show the time. The sun, as it moves across the sky, casts a shadow on the

Below, the Egyptian water clock. Dating from around 1400 B.C., it was simply a bowl that leaked water at an even rate. The water level marked time as it fell below lines drawn in the bowl. Opposite, sand glasses, dated 1720, from China.

Below, an escapement is used in all mechanical clocks to control the gears. The verge escapement (1) was used until the late 1800s when the anchor or recoil escapement (2) was invented. Galileo was the first person to show that a pendulum could control the movement of the escapement.

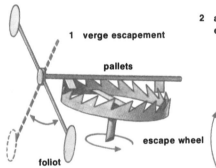

1 verge escapement

pallets

foliot

escape wheel

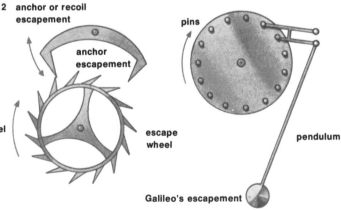

2 anchor or recoil escapement

anchor escapement

escape wheel

pins

pendulum

Galileo's escapement

Left, a 17th century Dutch domestic clock. Below, Harrison's chronometer, a device used by British sailors. In 1764, after a trip to the Barbados, it lost five seconds.

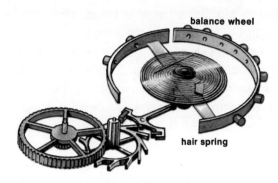

balance wheel

hair spring

escape wheel

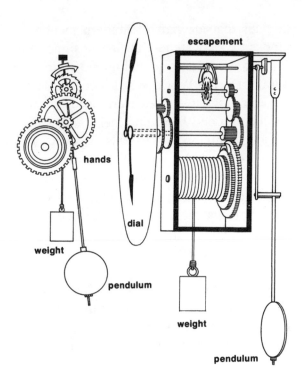

escapement

hands

dial

weight

pendulum

weight

pendulum

The diagrams, above, show the basic parts of a clock and how they work. The weight-driven clock has a constant power, while the clock with a spring may run down.

Above, the balance wheel and balance, or hair spring, of a modern watch. Left, a balance spring from a watch. The regulator of the watch is a balance wheel. The wheel is made to swing back and forth by a delicate spring. One end of the spring is fastened to the wheel and the other to the body of the watch. The wheel engages the escapement.

The electric alarm clock, above, is powered by a direct current cell. An oscillator converts the direct current into alternating current, which drives the electric motor.

The atomic clock, right, is even more accurate than the electronic clock. The atomic clock uses the vibrations of atoms of cesium, a metal, as its time marker, rather than gears.

dial. A sundial tells time by measuring the length or the angle of the shadow.

Other devices that were once used to tell time include candle clocks, water clocks, and hourglasses. With candle clocks, time was measured by the rate of a burning candle. The water clock was a leaking bowl. The hours were noted as the water surface dropped past lines marked inside the bowl. In the hourglass, sand flowed from one container into another at a steady rate. By measuring the amount of sand in either container, a person could tell how much time had passed.

Historians believe the first mechanical clocks were made by a number of inventors during the late 1200s. These clocks, working by a system of weights, had no hands or pendulum. They had a bell that rang to mark the hour. The word "clock" probably comes from the French word *cloche* or the German word *Glocke,* both of which mean "bell." The dial and hour hand had been added by the middle 1300s. The first clocks that worked by a system of springs are thought to have been developed in the late 1400s.

During the 1600s, Christian Huygens, a Dutch physicist, worked out the conditions for perfect oscillation (back and forth movement) of a pendulum. A balance wheel and balance spring were invented in the 1670s, widely replacing the pendulum. In this type of instrument, one end of the spring is fixed. The other end follows the backward and forward motion of the balance wheel. The spring winds and unwinds as the wheel swings. The manufacture of smaller clocks and watches started around the middle 1600s. Early watches had only an hour hand and were made in unusual shapes, including skulls and crosses. By the late 1600s, some watches had a minute hand. These watches, commonly called pocket watches, were the most popular watch style for more than 200 years.

By the start of the 1700s, minute hands became common. By the middle of the century, inventors had developed most of the devices that are part of modern mechanical clocks. Wristwatches, at first designed only for women, became common in the late 1800s. During World War I, because of convenience, wristwatches were used by men.

The second hand on clocks and watches became common in the 1900s. Electric clocks were common by the 1920s. Quartz-based clocks appeared by the 1930s. The first atomic clock was invented in the 1940s. Electric dial watches were introduced in the 1950s. Digital clocks and watches became popular in the 1970s.

Types of clocks in use today Modern clocks range from small, plain models to huge, decorative works of art. Dial clocks have hands that show the time by pointing to numbers on a dial. Digital clocks show the time in numbers on the clock face. Every clock has two main parts, the case and the movement, or works, inside the case. In addition to showing time, the movement supplies power to run the clock. The movement also "keeps time." Timekeeping in most clocks is based on the frequency (rate) of some repeated action, such as the action of a pendulum or spring device as mentioned earlier. Atomic clocks are based on the vibrations of certain atoms or molecules. Atomic clocks are the most accurate clocks ever made, estimated to gain or lose only a few seconds in 100,000 years.

The two main types of clocks are mechanical clocks and electric clocks. Mechanical clocks are powered by various devices that must be wound. Some mechanical clocks have to be wound every day. Some do not have to be wound for a week or more. Almost all mechanical clocks are dial clocks. Some are weight driven. Others are spring driven. Weight-driven clocks are powered by a weight that hangs from a chain or cord. When the clock is wound, the chain or cord gets wrapped around a drum. The weight is drawn up near the drum. Gravity pulls the weight

The largest four-sided clock in the world is found in Milwaukee, Wisconsin. Each of the four clock faces is forty feet wide, with a total weight of fifty tons. Large, many-sided clocks like this one may be seen in cities around the world. City clocks have been in use for centuries, since the times when people had no time-keeping devices that could be carried with them.

down. As the weight is lowered, the cord or chain slowly unwinds, turning the drum. The drum then turns a number of gear wheels. These wheels are connected in a series called a train. Each of these wheels turns at a specific speed. Certain wheels are attached to the hands of the clock. A pendulum and a device called the escapement work together to control the weight from being lowered too fast. The escapement is made up of an escape wheel and a verge. The escape wheel is connected to the train and turns when the clock runs. The pendulum, the time-keeping device of the clock, swings from side to side at a steady rate. As it swings, it tilts the verge from side to side. With each tilt, two hooks called pallets catch the escape wheel and stop it. When the pendulum swings back, the pallets release the wheel and the wheel turns slightly. This process regulates the wheels in the train. It also causes the "tick-tock" sound.

In spring-driven clocks, the mainspring gets wound up when the clock is wound. The mainspring unwinds slowly. This motion turns the wheels in the train. Some spring-driven clocks have a battery that rewinds the mainspring automatically. The escapement in a spring-driven clock is similar to the escapement in a weight-driven clock. But many spring-driven clocks have a balance wheel instead of a pendulum. A coiled spring known as the balance spring, or hairspring, is connected to the balance wheel. This spring coils and uncoils. Such action makes the balance wheel swing back and forth at a steady rate.

The second main group of clocks, electric clocks, can be battery powered or line powered. Battery powered clocks have a balance wheel or a pendulum that controls their speed. Others have a tuning fork or a tiny bar of quartz crystal. Receiving power from the battery, a tuning fork or crystal vibrates with high, steady frequencies. Quartz-based clocks contain an electric circuit. (*See* CIRCUIT, ELECTRIC.) This circuit changes the number of vibrations into time information. Most of these quartz clocks are accurate to within 60 seconds a year.

A line-powered clock gets its power from an electric outlet. The current from the outlet also regulates the clock's speed. The flow of alternating current changes its direction 120 times per second. A motor usually counts the changes in direction, using this information to control the time. Most digital clocks are line powered. In some digital clocks, the digits are printed on moving tapes or on flip cards. Others have a liquid crystal display. This type uses digits that reflect the light around it. A light-emitting diode display has digits shaped from electronic devices called diodes, which give off light.

Types of watches in use today Most modern watches are wristwatches, but pocket watches are still used. Other watches are mounted in pins, rings, or necklaces. Watches, like clocks, vary greatly from plain models costing about $10 to more decorative models costing more than $50,000. The two main groups of watches are dial or digital, based on how they show the time. Dial watches show time by hands on the watch face. The two kinds of dial watches are mechanical watches and electric watches. Mechanical watches, powered by a mainspring, work in the same way as mechanical clocks. Electric watches get their power from a tiny battery.

Digital watches are quartz-based and have no moving parts. The circuits in a digital watch change the time information directly into an electric digital display on the watch face. As in digital clocks, digital watches have two main kinds of electric displays, the liquid crystal display, or LCD, and the light-emitting diode display, or LED. Diodes use more power than the LCD's. To save power, LED watches show the time only when the person turns on the display. More than 50 million watches are sold in the United States every year.   J.J.A./R.W.L.

CLONE (klōn) A clone is a group of organisms with identical genetic structures. (*See* GENE.) Except for a rare mutation, they are also exactly alike in appearance. A clone descends from a single parent by asexual reproduction. A colony of bacteria is a clone because each of the millions of bacteria has descended from a single bacterium by a splitting process called fission. (*See* ASEXUAL REPRODUCTION.)

Simple plants such as algae and fungi reproduce asexually and can produce a clone. Higher plants also produce clones by vegetative propagation. Cloning is important to farmers so they can continue to produce plants such as certain varieties of apples, oranges, and potatoes, which have desirable characteristics. Strawberries produce clones naturally by sending out specialized, underground stems called stolons. Each stolon produces many new plants.

Some animals, such as sponges and hydra, can reproduce asexually or undergo regeneration to produce a clone. Frogs and salamanders have been cloned by destroying the nucleus of an egg and replacing it with the nucleus of any body cell from another organism of the same species. The egg develops into an adult with all the characteristics of the donor.

The word "clone" is also used to describe an organism or tissue of an organism that is artificially produced using the organism's DNA. In the mid-1970s, a technique was developed for transferring genes from one organism to another. This involved adding DNA from a plant or animal cell to the DNA in bacteria. Scientists have already found practical applications for this technique. They have used it to produce useful forms of new bacteria. (*See* GENETICS.) Medical researchers have used the technique to produce vital hormones such as insulin for the treatment of diabetes and growth hormone for treatment of growth deficiencies in children.

Since each DNA molecule contains an organism's entire genetic code, it is theoretically possible that a new organism could be "grown" from one of its DNA molecules. (*See* DNA.) In the future it is possible that certain organs and tissues could be cloned. A heart patient may be able to receive a transplant of a clone of his own heart, avoiding any rejection problems. (*See* TRANSPLANTATION.) A dentist may be able to replace decayed teeth with new, cloned teeth. Research into cloning and genetic engineering is just beginning to explore the medical and other possibilities that may be of great benefit in the years to come. *See also* HEREDITY.

                    A.J.C./E.R.L.

CLOUD (klaůd) A cloud is a mass of water droplets or ice crystals that floats in the air. Air contains water vapor that is evaporated from the oceans, lakes, and rivers. (*See* EVAPORATION.) Warm air can hold more water vapor than cold air.

For each 1 km [0.6 mi] rise in the atmosphere, the temperature drops by about 10°C [18°F]. If a mountain lies in the path of the wind, the air rises up the side of the mountain. As the air rises, it cools, and cannot hold as much water vapor. At a temperature known as the dew point, the water vapor condenses, forming water droplets. These water droplets may remain liquid below the freezing point, 0°C [32°F]. If this occurs, they are called supercooled. (*See* SUPERCOOLING.) In clouds high up in the atmosphere, where the temperature is below −40°C [−40°F], the water droplets become ice crystals. Rain and snow fall from clouds of supercooled water droplets and ice crystals.

CLASSIFICATION OF CLOUDS			
Height (figures refer to temperate latitudes)	Type of Cloud	Symbol	Description
Low Clouds Up to 8,000 ft.	Stratus	St	Uniform, gray cloud layer. May cover high ground.
	Cumulus	Cu	Detached heaps of cloud, considerable vertical development. Brilliant white when lit by the sun. Fairly horizontal base, but bulging upper parts.
	Cumulonimbus	Cb	The thundercloud. Dense, with the upper portion often flattened like an anvil. Its base may be very dark.
	Nimbostratus	Ns	Gray, often dark, layer of cloud, sometimes blurred by falling rain or snow.
	Stratocumulus	Sc	Grayish white sheet of cloud, with definite shading. Composed of rounded masses which sometimes merge.
Medium Clouds 8,000-15,000 ft.	Altocumulus	Ac	Grayish white sheet or patch of cloud, with definite shading. Composed of rounded masses, often merged.
	Altostratus	As	Grayish sheet of cloud, either fibrous or uniform in appearance. Often produces the "watery" sky seen before depressions.
High Clouds Above 15,000 ft.	Cirrocumulus	Cc	Thin sheet or patch of cloud in the form of ripples or rounded small masses, often merged together.
	Cirrostratus	Cs	Transparent film of fibrous, whitish cloud. Often seen before a depression. It is often the cause of the "halo" seen around the sun or moon, which it produces by the effect of light on ice crystals.
	Cirrus	Ci	Delicate white, detached clouds with fibrous appearance. Its many forms include "mares' tails."

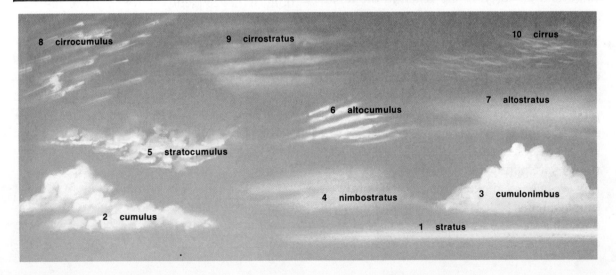

8 cirrocumulus
9 cirrostratus
10 cirrus
7 altostratus
6 altocumulus
5 stratocumulus
4 nimbostratus
3 cumulonimbus
2 cumulus
1 stratus

This view of the earth as photographed from space clearly shows patterns of cloud formations. Africa is in the upper portion of the picture.

There are two major cloud types. Cumuliform clouds are puffy white clouds. They have a flat bottom and are often very tall. When cumuliform clouds grow very tall and dark, they are called cumulonimbus clouds, or thunderheads. The other important cloud type is stratiform clouds. Stratiform clouds are long blanket clouds that form in layers. They often bring rain or snow. Ten important cloud types are listed in the table. *See also* METEOROLOGY.   J.M.C./C.R.

CLOVE (klōv) The clove (*Caryophyllus aromaticus*) is a tropical, evergreen tree that produces flower buds which are dried and used as a spice. The tree grows as tall as 12 m [40 ft] and has large, pointed leaves. The flowers are purple and grow in clusters. If the flower bud is picked and dried before it blooms, it can be used to make a powder or an oil with a strong odor and a sharp taste. Oil of cloves is used as a flavoring for cakes and candies and is also used as a dental anesthetic. Clove buds are used to flavor hams and other foods.   A.J.C./M.H.S.

CLOVER (klō′ vər) Clover is the name given to more than 300 species of herbaceous plants that belong to the pea family. These legumes grow wild in fields throughout temperate areas of the northern hemisphere and in South Africa and South America. Clover is often cultivated as a food for livestock. Since clover is an excellent agent of nitrogen fixation, it is frequently plowed back into the ground to enrich the soil.

Red clover is the most important variety of clover. Though it is a perennial, it usually dies after two or three years. Red clover may grow as tall as 60 cm [24 in] and can be pollinated only by a bumblebee. (*See* POLLINATION.) Other common types of clover are white clover, crimson clover, and strawberry clover.

Clover usually has three leaves attached at their bases. Four-leaf clovers have long been considered a sign of good luck by some people.   A.J.C./M.H.S.

Above, a thick patch of clover. Clover is a member of the pea family, and is a valuable plant for farmers.

CLUB MOSS (kləb mȯs)

A club moss is any of more than 1,200 species of small, evergreen plants growing in damp forests and on tropical mountains. A member of the genus *Lycopodium*, the club moss is not a true moss. The club moss produces an underground root that grows near the surface for about 3 m [10 ft]. Green stems and branches grow from this root and may extend 10 cm [4 in] above the surface. These branches are densely covered with small, needlelike leaves. Cones may grow in clusters. These cones contain spores used in asexual reproduction. The asexual phase alternates with a sexual phase, an underground, gamete-producing generation. (*See* ALTERNATION OF GENERATIONS.)

During the Carboniferous period, club mosses grew to heights of 30 m [100 ft]. Their remains are an important part of coal. *See also* FERN; HORSETAIL. A.J.C./M.H.S.

Above, tiny club mosses, members of the genus *Lycopodium*. These are not true mosses.

CLUTCH (kləch)

A clutch is a device that is used to transmit power from an engine to a drive shaft. It makes it possible to keep an engine running even though the drive shaft has stopped turning. This is more efficient than stopping the engine each time the shaft is stopped.

Clutches can be found on many familiar objects including farm and factory machinery, clothes washers, dishwashers, sewing machines, power lawnmowers, and bicycles. The most familiar clutch, however, is the one used in automobiles. The driver of a car needs some device to disconnect the engine from the drive wheels in stop-and-go traffic and to shift gears. The clutch does this job. There are two types of automobile clutches, the friction clutch and the fluid clutch.

The friction clutch consists of one metal disk pressed tightly between two other disks. It is operated by a foot pedal controlled by the driver. The disk in the middle is called the clutch plate. It is connected to a shaft leading into the transmission. The transmission contains sets of gears that allow the drive shaft to turn at various speeds. The other two disks in the friction clutch are the flywheel, which is mounted on the engine crankshaft, and the pressure plate. The pressure plate is attached to the clutch shaft. When the driver takes his foot off the clutch pedal to engage the clutch, powerful springs push the pressure plate toward the flywheel. The pressure plate holds the clutch plate tightly against the flywheel. Friction between the clutch plate and the rotating flywheel causes the clutch plate to turn. The clutch shaft on which it is mounted rotates and transmits power to the transmission. When the driver pushes down on the clutch pedal to disengage the clutch, the pressure plate and clutch plate move away from the flywheel.

The fluid, or hydraulic, clutch is used on all cars that have automatic transmissions. It automatically engages and disengages the clutch and thus eliminates the foot pedal. The fluid clutch is linked electrically to the gearshift lever and the engine. It operates automatically when the driver moves the gearshift lever to change gears, or when the engine requires gear changes because of the speed at which the car is moving. The fluid clutch is contained in a housing that looks like a large doughnut. Disks containing a series of fanlike blades are mounted inside the housing. The disk closest to the engine is connected to the engine crankshaft. When the crankshaft turns, this disk turns. Another disk is connected to a shaft leading into the transmission. The housing is filled with oil, called hydraulic fluid. When the driver moves the gearshift lever, the front disk begins to turn. Its blades are positioned so that they spin the oil toward the other disk. The second disk's blades are positioned so that the spinning oil, or fluid, forces the disk to turn in the same direction as the first disk. The driven disk, or the one nearest the transmission, can never turn quite as fast as the disk connected to the engine crankshaft because the fluid action has a bit of "give," or slack, in it. That is why it is possible for a car with a fluid clutch to stand still while the engine is running slowly even though the transmission is in gear. The fluid clutch also smooths out jerks caused by the shifting of gears or sudden changes in speed. *See also* AUTOMOBILE; HYDRAULICS.

W.R.P./J.T.

CNIDARIA (nī da′ rē ə) Cnidaria is a phylum of the animal kingdom. The phylum is sometimes called Coelenterata. The sea anemone, coral, jellyfish, and hydra are members of Cnidaria. They range in size from microscopic to nearly 2 m [6.6 ft] in diameter. Cnidarians are very simple animals. They are the next to the lowest group of animals that have cells organized into tissue.

The body of a Cnidarian is a hollow sac. The animal brings in food and removes waste through the one opening in the body. The opening is usually surrounded by arms called tentacles. These tentacles capture food and bring it into the opening, where it is eaten. Cnidarians eat small invertebrates and fishes. Some Cnidarians have stinging cells called nematocysts on their tentacles. The nematocysts look like little spears. If a small animal touches the tentacles, the nematocysts shoot out and either spear or wrap around the prey. They often inject a poison which kills or paralyzes the animal. The nematocysts of jellyfish and Portuguese men-of-war sting swimmers who brush against them.

Cnidarians can reproduce sexually or asexually. (*See* REPRODUCTION.) When they reproduce sexually, there are two different life stages. A polyp is a saclike structure that anchors to a rock in water and looks like a plant. When polyps reproduce, they create medusas, which look like jellyfish. These medusas swim through the water, settle on a rock, and form other polyps. *See also* ALTERNATION OF GENERATIONS; CLASSIFICATION OF LIVING ORGANISMS.

S.R.G./R.J.B.

COAL

Coal (kōl) is a naturally occurring accumulation of vegetable matter. It has been changed by heat and pressure over a long period of time into a lightweight, black to brown, rocklike material. Coal provides heat and power for many industries. It is also used as a source of raw materials for the chemical industry. The United States produces more coal than any other country except the Soviet Union. Forty percent of the world coal supply is located in North America.

Coal formation Large quantities of coal formed during a time called the Carboniferous period, about 250 million years ago. Parts of the earth were then covered by swamplike seas. Because of the hot, moist climate, gigantic plants were able to grow. When the

This prehistoric scene shows a cross section of the earth as well as plants and animals that were then living on the earth. Within these layers of rock, dead plants and animals have already begun to change to fossil fuels.

In one operation, this continuous miner removes coal from a mine wall and then loads the coal into a shuttle car, which takes the coal to the surface.

plants died, they sank into the swamp, and new plants replaced them. As the newer plants died, layers of dead material began to form. Mud and sand settled on top of this layer and pressed some of the water out. Eventually the land rose and more plants grew on the surface. These new plants died, decayed, and were covered by sediment again. This cycle continued for millions of years. Many layers of stratified matter formed as decaying material was forced further beneath the surface. (*See* STRATIFICATION.) Great pressure was produced by these many layers. The pressure, together with chemical reactions, gradually transformed the decayed material into coal. This is why coal is called a fossil fuel. Sometimes, the outline of an ancient plant can be seen in a lump of coal.

Kinds of coal Coal consists mainly of carbon, hydrogen, oxygen, and nitrogen. Coal has no chemical formula because the elements that compose it appear in different ratios. Coal is classified by geologists as sedimentary rock.

There are several different types of coal. Peat is a material in the first stages of coal

formation. When removed from the ground, it may contain as much as 90% water. Peat must be dried out before use. Dry peat contains up to 60% carbon.

Lignite contains about 50% water. It is a brown or black coal. Dry lignite is 60 to 75% carbon. Black lignite is often called subbituminous coal and may be more than 80% carbon.

Bituminous coal is the most common type of coal containing up to 80% carbon. It has many industrial uses as well as being an important fuel. Most of the bituminous coal mined in the United States comes from the area just west of the Appalachian Mountains.

Anthracite is the final product of the coal formation process. It contains very little water, but is about 95% carbon. Most anthracite is mined in eastern Pennsylvania. Almost half of the anthracite produced is used for heating. It is the most expensive type of coal.

Coal mining Coal is usually mined in one of two ways: strip (surface) mining or underground mining.

Strip mining is done by removing the dirt above a coal deposit. When the coal is exposed, explosives are used to break it up. The coal is then loaded into trucks and taken away. Although strip mining is an efficient way of obtaining coal, it has a damaging effect on the ecology of the region.

Underground mining reaches coal deposits deep below the surface. In a shaft mine, a hole is dug straight down to the coal. Air for the miners is provided by ventilation shafts. Practically all of the coal is mined using machines and explosives. The coal removed from the deposit is loaded into a wagonlike car and lifted to the surface. The miners enter and leave the shaft by elevator.

Another method of underground mining is called slope mining. Slope mining is used to reach coal deposits in hillsides. A sloped tunnel leads from the outside to the coal deposit. Trains are used to move the coal, as well as to transport the miners in and out of the mine. *See also* MINING.　　　　J.M.C./R.H.

COAL GAS (kōl gas) Coal gas is a fuel composed mainly of hydrogen and methane. It is obtained when coal is heated in the absence of air. The coal is heated in large, air-

Below, a diagram showing how coal gas is made, from powdered coal to purified gas.

tight ovens called retorts. The lack of air prevents the coal from burning. When the temperature reaches 1200° to 1300°C [2200° to 2400°F], the coal gives off vapors and gases and changes to coke. These vapors and gases are treated to remove important by-products of carbonization, like tar, ammonia, and hydrogen sulfide. The tar is condensed by cooling, while the ammonia is dissolved in a series of water sprays, called scrubbers. (*See* CONDENSATION.) Coal gas is stored in large containers, called gasometers. It is burned to produce heat for factories and homes. *See also* COKE.

J.M.C./R.H.

COAST (kōst) The coast is the land next to the sea. Waves are always changing the shape of the coast. In some places, the waves wear away, or erode, the coast. In other places they pile up, or deposit, material to form new land. (*See* EROSION.)

The changing level of the sea has a great effect on the coast. Since the Ice Age, water

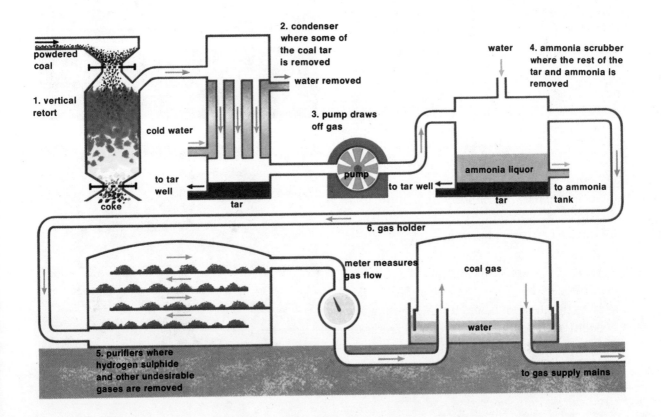

from melted ice has made the oceans much deeper and has flooded many coasts. In some places, earth movements have caused the coastlines to emerge, or rise out of the water. For example, the east coast of the United States emerged from the sea and later partially submerged. A submerged coastline is one that has sunk into the sea. Submerged coasts often have long shallow inlets called rias, river valleys that have filled with water.

Coastal erosion Though the ocean may seem calm, sand and pebbles are always moving and rubbing against each other. This motion grinds down the sand and pebbles to much smaller particles. During storms, large waves trap air in holes and cracks in the rock along the shoreline. When the air is released, it may have enough force to break apart the rock. Storm waves can also lift up pebbles and rocks and throw them against the shore. This may undercut cliffs to form caves. Soft rock erodes faster than hard rock. On coasts where there are both soft and hard rocks, the soft rock may erode completely, leaving the hard rock sticking out into the sea. This leftover hard rock is called headland. When two caves meet in a headland, a natural arch is formed. If the arch falls, a pillar of rock called a stack remains.

Coastal deposition Some material that either erodes from coasts or is carried into the sea by rivers may be deposited elsewhere. It may form a beach or new land area. But in places where the water is moving in more than one direction, the eroded material builds up into long, narrow ridges called spits. Spits occur most often in bays at the mouth of a river. When a spit cuts a bay off from the ocean, it is called a baymouth bar. Tombolos are spits that link an island to the mainland or connect two islands. Spits and bars are common along the east coast of the United States and the east coast of England. *See also* OCEANOGRAPHY.   J.M.C./W.R.S.

Coasts where material is deposited contrast with coasts that are eroded. Above, a shingle pit in Scotland is an example of deposition. Right, the sea wears away the base of cliffs in Scotland. Below, arches and a stack are the result of sea erosion in Dorset, England. Bottom, a cave blowhole in England.

COBALT (kō' bòlt') Cobalt (Co) is a silver white metallic element. Its atomic number is 27. Its atomic weight is 58.94. Cobalt melts at 1495°C [2723°F] and boils at 2900°C [5252°F]. In 1737, George Brandt, a Swedish chemist, discovered cobalt.

Cobalt got its name from the German word *kobold,* meaning "underground spirit." Cobalt is found mainly in Canada and Australia. The metal is usually found in compounds with sulfur and arsenic.

Cobalt alloys are used to make parts for jet engines and for cutting tools. Because cobalt has strong magnetic properties, its alloys are also used to make magnets. (*See* MAGNETISM.) Many cobalt compounds are used as pigments, especially in ceramics. Cobalt-60 is a strongly radioactive isotope used in medicine for treating diseases. This treatment is called radiation therapy. (*See* RADIOACTIVITY.)   J.J.A./J.R.W.

COBRA (kō'brə) The cobra is a poisonous snake that belongs to the family Elapidae. It lives in Africa and southern Asia, though the greater variety of cobras is to be found in Africa.

Cobras are often called "hooded snakes." When one is excited or has been disturbed, it raises the front part of its body and spreads some of its ribs. This flattens the cobra's neck and makes it look as if the snake were wearing a hood.

The Indian cobra grows to about 2 m [6 ft] in length and ranges in color from a yellowish to a dark brown. It is sometimes called the "spectacled cobra" because the marks on the back of its hood look like a pair of eyeglasses.

The spitting cobra of Africa "spits" its poison, or venom, in an outward, jetlike stream toward the eyes of its victim. The poison can be sprayed over a distance of eight feet and can cause extreme irritation, blindness, or even death if the victim is not treated immediately.

The longest of all poisonous snakes, the king cobra, lives in southeastern Asia. It sometimes grows to a length of 5.5 m [18 ft]. Because of its length, when it raises itself and spreads its hood it is a spectacular sight. The king cobra is mostly olive-green and is believed, by some people, to be trainable.

All true cobras lay eggs instead of giving birth to live young.

The cobra is the natural enemy of animals such as fishes, birds, and frogs because they make up the cobra's diet. The natural enemy of the cobra is the mongoose. (*See* MONGOOSE.)   H.G./R.L.L.

When cobras are disturbed, they rear up and expand their necks to form a "hood." The Indian cobra, right, is found throughout southern Asia, from the Caspian Sea to the Philippines, and as far south as Bali in Indonesia. This poisonous snake is often used by snake charmers. The cobra does not hear the music of the charmer, because snakes are deaf. However, it reacts to the movements of the charmer, feeling them through the earth.

COCA PLANT (kō' kə plant) The coca plant (*Erythroxylon coca*) is one of a group of South American trees and shrubs. It may grow as tall as 2 m [6.6 ft] and produces small leaves 2.5 to 7.6 cm [1 to 3 in] long. Some Peruvian and Bolivian Indians chew the leaves to help fight hunger and fatigue. The leaves cause numbness of the lips and mouth when chewed because they contain several drugs, including cocaine. (*See* ALKALOID.)

Cocaine was once used by doctors as an anesthetic. It is used illegally to produce a feeling of happiness and well-being. Frequent and regular use can cause a strong psychological addiction, though probably not a physical addiction. Since cocaine is usually inhaled through the nose, it may cause damage to the cartilage of the septum of the nose.

A.J.C./F.W.S.

COCKATOO (käk′ ə tü′) A cockatoo is a large bird that belongs to the parrot family Psittacidae. It is found in the forests of Australia, New Guinea, the Philippines, and nearby islands. Cockatoos are usually light colored, but a few are black. They have long feathers which stick up on their heads. Cockatoos breed readily in captivity and often are kept as pets.

S.R.G./L.L.S.

Cockatoos are members of the parrot family.

COCKLE (käk′ əl) A cockle is a saltwater animal that belongs to the class Pelecypoda of the Mollusca phylum. It is a bivalve. Its soft, fleshy body is enclosed by two hard shells that are hinged together to open like a book. Cockles live in the sand on the bottom of the ocean, sometimes 1000 m [3,280 ft] below sea surface. They are, however, most common in shallow, coastal waters. They feed by strain-

ing little particles out of the water they suck into their shells. Some species of cockles are eaten by man.

S.R.G./C.S.H.

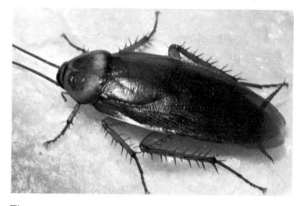

The cockroach is a common, adaptable insect.

COCKROACH (käk′ rōch′) The cockroach is any of more than 3,500 species of insects belonging to the order Blattaria. They are related to crickets, grasshoppers, and mantids. Cockroaches have flattened bodies covered with hard but elastic casings. Their four wings are folded flat on the back. They have two hairlike antennae and long, strong legs covered with bristles. Cockroaches vary in appearance, but the most common varieties (*Periplaneta americana* and *Blattella germanica*) are brown and 1 to 3 cm [0.4 to 1.2 in] long.

Most cockroaches live outdoors under rocks or logs, or in decaying bark or leaves. A few species, however, have invaded houses, bakeries, shops, and groceries, and eat almost anything. Their diets consist of animal and vegetable matter, garbage, and other insects. Cockroaches reproduce quickly in moist, dark places. They avoid bright light and usually hunt for food at night.

The female cockroach carries many eggs in a purse-shaped, hard-walled capsule which she hides in a damp, protected place. Once the eggs hatch, the young force their way out of the capsule. Some roaches bear live young. As the young grow, they molt several times before becoming adults. (*See* METAMORPHOSIS; MOLTING.)

The tree above shows green — not yet ripe — coconuts.

Cockroaches have been on earth for millions of years. Fossil remains from the Carboniferous period have been found, indicating that cockroaches have changed very little in the past 300 million years. Cockroaches are so highly adaptable that there seems to be little chance that they will be eliminated in the near future. A.J.C./J.R.

COCONUT (kō′ kə nət′) The coconut (*Cocos nucifera*) is a tall tree on which the coconut fruit grows. The coconut is cultivated on sandy soil in tropical areas throughout the world. Reaching a height of 30 m [100 ft], this palm has large leaves, 5 m [16.5 ft] long, growing at the top of the tree. (*See* PALM FAMILY.) The coconut fruits grow in clusters among the leaves. Each fruit takes about a year to mature, and each tree can produce about 100 fruits a year.

The coconut fruit is a seed enclosed in a thick husk and rind which are, in turn, enclosed in a woody shell. The seed itself is 20 to 30 cm [8 to 12 in] long and 15 to 25 cm [6 to 10 in] in diameter. It is made of sweet, white meat surrounded by a thin, brown skin. The hollow center is filled with coconut milk. Dried coconut meat is called copra. It can be shredded for use in candies and other desserts, or processed to produce a valuable oil used for cooking and many other purposes.

In addition to the fruit, the coconut tree has great value. Its wood is used for buildings and furniture. The leaves and bark are used for roofs, mats, and baskets. The sap is used to make sugar and an alcoholic beverage.

A.J.C./F.W.S.

COD (käd) A cod is a saltwater fish that belongs to the family Gadidae. This family of several species is a very important group of food fishes. Cod are widely distributed in deep, cold, northern waters. One of the best places to catch the Atlantic cod commercially is the Grand Banks, off Newfoundland, Canada. Cod may reach 1.8 m [6 ft] in length and 91 kg [200 lb] in weight. S.R.G./E.C.M.

Cod is an important food fish.

COELACANTH (sē′ lə kanth′) A coelacanth is a large, saltwater fish that belongs to the family Coelacanthidae. The coelacanth was thought to be extinct until 1938 when a fisherman caught one in his nets off the coast of South Africa. Since then, a few of the primitive fish have been caught. Biologists do not know how common the coelacanth is because it lives in deep waters where nets cannot reach. Coelacanths were very numerous on earth 300 to 700 million years ago. Many fossil coelacanths have been found. S.R.G./E.C.M.

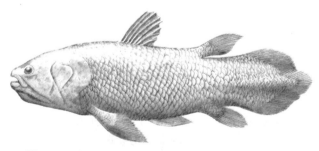

The coelacanth is a prehistoric fish that was thought to be extinct, until found in 1938.

COELENTERATE *See* CNIDARIA.

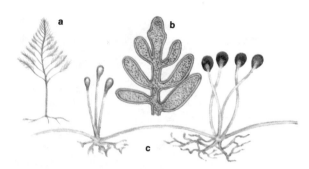

The coenocyte *Bryopsis* is a single cell. Detail (b) shows part of this cell. The fungus *Rhizopus* (c) is also a single cell.

COENOCYTE (sē′ nə sīt′) A coenocyte is a cell with more than one nucleus. When most cells multiply, one nucleus is created for each new cell. A cell wall is formed between the different cells. Coenocytes create new nuclei without forming more cell walls. The cell simply grows larger. It contains many identical nuclei. Many fungi and green algae are coenocytic. (*See* FUNGUS.) *See also* MITOSIS. S.R.G./E.R.L.

COFFEE (kȯ′ fē) Coffee is a drink made from the roasted and ground beans of the coffee tree, *Coffea arabica*. *Coffea arabica* is a shrub belonging to the madder family Rubiaceae. It has glossy, green leaves and white flowers. *Coffea arabica* grows from 4.3 to 6.1 m [14 to 20 ft] high, but most coffee growers prune it to 3.7 m [12 ft]. It is cultivated in tropical climates in Java, Sumatra, South America, equatorial Africa, Arabia, Hawaii, Mexico, Central America, and the West Indies.

Coffee trees are usually five years old before they begin to bear a full crop of coffee berries. The average tree bears enough berries each year to make about 0.7 kg [1.5 lb] of roasted coffee. Coffee trees grow best at altitudes of 610 to 1,800 m [2,000 to 6,000 ft].

History One legend about the discovery of coffee says that it was discovered over 2,000 years ago by goatherds in Ethiopia. They noticed that their flocks were staying awake all night after eating the leaves and berries of coffee trees. The drink later became popular in Arabia in the 1200s. It was introduced into Turkey and Italy in the 1600s. Soon, coffeehouses, restaurants that serve coffee and light snacks, began to spring up all over Europe. They became popular places for people to meet for serious discussions. Coffeehouses still fill that role. Colonists brought coffee to the United States in 1660. Coffee growing became a major industry in Brazil in the 1700s.

The coffee bean Coffee berries contain two beans, or seeds. The berries are picked by hand. No one has yet found a way to harvest them by machine. The beans are removed from the berries and roasted at 482°C [900°F] for 16 to 17 minutes. Then they are stored in 60 kg [132 lb] amounts in burlap bags to await grinding. Food processors grind the beans into drip, regular, or fine grades. Then they pack the ground coffee in vacuum cans or paper bags, for sale in the markets.

Coffee tree grows in warm, dry climates. Above, the dark red berries, containing two seeds, which are the coffee beans. Left, a mass of coffee beans is dried in the hot sun.

Brewing coffee Coffee is brewed in percolators, drip pots, or vacuum coffee makers, which strain boiling water through the coffee grounds. Some models use paper filters to keep grounds out of the finished coffee. The most popular brewing formula is two tablespoons of roast coffee for each cup of coffee desired. Freshly brewed coffee has a rich, appetizing aroma that adds to the pleasure of drinking it. Coffee contains caffeine, a drug that acts as a stimulant. The drink tends to expand blood vessels mildly so that more blood flows to the heart and brain. Because of this, coffee has become the universal ''wake up'' drink. Many people find that drinking coffee prevents them from going to sleep at night.

Instant coffee Instant coffee is coffee that does not have to go through the brewing process. Powdered and freeze-dried coffee crystals are simply added to boiling water. It is ready to drink immediately. Powdered instant coffee is made by brewing large containers of coffee and evaporating the water from the brew so that powder crystals remain. Freeze-dried instant coffee is made by freezing freshly brewed coffee into slabs. The slabs are ground into chunks and placed in pressurized chambers. Moisture in the form of ice is drawn off, leaving coffee crystals, or tiny chunks, that average 1 cubic millimeter in size.

Café espresso, also called café expresso, is a strong coffee that is made by forcing live steam under pressure, or boiling water, through dark-roast ground coffee. It is usually served in tiny cups, and it is meant to be sipped very slowly. Cafe espresso was first made popular in Italy.

Decaffeinated coffee is coffee that has had its caffeine removed by chemical means. It tastes the same as regular coffee. Some people prefer decaffeinated coffee for health reasons.

Coffee in the U.S. The United States is the largest consumer of coffee in the world. Americans drink about 400 million cups a day. Millions of U.S. workers pause once or twice a day for coffee breaks. The coffee break has become an accepted tradition in the business world. Each American consumes about 5 kg [12 lb] of coffee annually. Overall, the U.S. consumes 1,180,000,000 kg [2,600,000,000 lb] each year. That is one third of all coffee produced annually in the world.

Most of the coffee sold in American markets is blended coffee. Coffee processors blend, or mix, various types together in the grinding process to achieve certain tastes. Sometimes they add other substances like chicory. Coffee sold in the southern part of the U.S. often contains chicory because many people in that region like the taste. Coffee processors import over 100 types of coffees. They can be classified into three general groups: Brazils, milds, and robusticas. Brazils are coffees grown in Brazil. Milds are coffees grown outside of Brazil that come from the *Coffea arabica* tree. Robusticas are coffees grown in Africa. Some coffee is named for the port from which it is shipped. Mocha coffee, for example, comes from the port of Mocha (Al Mukhá) in Yemen.

Coffee is vital to the economies of many Latin countries. Brazil, the largest single coffee grower in the world, produces 1,126,000,000 kg [2,482,000,000 lb] annually. Colombia, a South American country, produces 512,000,000, kg [1,129,000,000 lb] each year. It is the second largest producer.

Coffee exporting countries have tried to control coffee prices for years. The United Nations helped arrange the International Coffee Agreement in 1963. It limits the price of coffee on the world market and places certain restrictions on amounts stored and shipped by each country. W.R.P./F.W.S.

COHERENT LIGHT (kō hir′ ənt līt′) When light waves of the same frequency travel in the same direction, they combine with and amplify each other. This is called coherent light. In effect, a light wave that is very long and continuous and has a sharply defined frequency is said to be coherent (sometimes called time-coherent). This can be seen in lasers. Lasers work on the principle of stimulated emission. In stimulated emission, a light wave or pulse passing by an excited atom (one that has greater energy than normal) causes that atom to give off energy. This energy is in the form of a light pulse, or a photon, that is exactly in step with the original wave. This effect builds up rapidly to give a very narrow, intense light beam.

Incoherent light, such as from ordinary light bulbs and fluorescent tubes, results from spontaneous emission. In spontaneous emission, excited atoms give off light in different directions and at different frequencies.

Two light waves are coherent if they are in step, like the members of a marching band or a column of well-trained soldiers. Incoherence could be likened to the random movements of members of a crowd going down the street from the stadium after a football game. *See also* LASER. J.M.C./S.S.B.

COHESION (kō hē′ zhən) Cohesion is the force that holds the molecules of a substance together. This force determines whether a substance is a solid, a liquid, or a gas. If the cohesion is strong, the molecules are tightly bound in place. The substance is then a solid. If the cohesion is very strong, the solid is hard. The cohesion is stronger in solids than in liquids. In gases the cohesion is even less. For example, ice has a strong cohesive force and does not change shape easily. Water has a weaker cohesive force than ice. Its shape depends on the shape of its container. Steam has very little cohesion. It expands to fill its container. This shows that cohesion decreases as the temperature of a substance increases. M.E./A.D.

COKE (kōk) Coke is a solid gray substance formed when coal is heated in an airtight oven, in a process called destructive distillation. The material that is volatile, or easily evaporated, is removed, leaving pores (little holes) in the coke. (*See* EVAPORATION.) Coke contains 87 to 90% carbon. Most coke produced is used for industrial purposes. Some of it is used to melt iron ore in a process called smelting. A small amount of coke is used as fuel. *See also* COAL.   J.M.C./J.M.

COLD-BLOODED ANIMAL (kōld′ bləd′ əd an′ ə məl)

Animals whose body temperatures change according to their surroundings are called cold-blooded animals. Another term for them is ectothermic animals. The body temperature of a cold-blooded animal is nearly the same as the air around it. Cold-blooded animals, therefore, cannot live in temperatures below freezing or they would freeze. Cold-blooded animals that live in areas with cold winters usually hibernate in places that do not freeze, such as the bottom of deep lakes. (*See* HIBERNATION.) During hot days, cold-blooded animals must stay in the shade to prevent becoming too hot. Snakes that live in deserts usually come out only at night. During mild days, cold-blooded animals will ''sun'' themselves to raise their body temperature. Turtles are often seen sunning themselves on a rock in a pond. *See also* METABOLISM; WARM-BLOODED ANIMAL.   S.R.G./R.J.B.

COLD, COMMON

The common cold (kōld) is the most widespread of all human diseases. It affects most people at some time in their lives. Many people suffer from colds several times a year, while others may go several years between colds. Since colds are caused by many different viruses, the body does not develop immunity, and antibiotics have little, if any, effect.

The symptoms of a common cold vary from mild discomfort to fever, body aches, and difficult breathing. The mucus membranes in the throat and nose become swollen. Often, the lungs and bronchial tubes become inflamed. A cold may last from 24 hours to several weeks.

Most doctors agree that a cold can be ''caught'' only from another person with a cold. When a patient coughs or sneezes, he releases viruses into the air. These viruses may be inhaled by another person in the area and cause him to become infected.

There is no treatment for a cold, only for the symptoms. Aspirin can help relieve body

A cold-blooded animal, the tuatara lives only on a few islands around New Zealand. It is the sole survivor of a group of ancient reptiles that lived between 250 and 70 million years ago. One of the tuatara's most interesting features is its third eye which is called the pineal eye. It is found on the top of the brain, with a hole in the skull just above it. In the adult tuatara, the skin thickens over the skull opening. This makes it unlikely that light from outside is detected by this eye. This eye may have been important in earlier reptiles, but its function in the tuatara is unknown.

aches, nasal sprays can reduce the swelling of the mucus membranes, making it easier to breathe. Many medications are sold to treat the various other symptoms of a cold. One of the major dangers of the common cold is that it weakens the body's defenses against other diseases.

There have been several vaccines developed against the common cold, but none has been effective. (*See* VACCINATION.) Dr. Linus Pauling has proposed that the use of vitamin C may be useful in preventing or treating a cold. His work has aroused much controversy. (*See* VITAMIN.) At present, the best way to treat a cold is to rest, drink plenty of fruit juices and other fluids, and have a balanced diet.   A.J.C./J.J.F.

COLLAGEN (käl′ ə jən) Collagen is the most common protein in the human body. It is a tough, fibrous material found in bone and connective tissue such as tendons, ligaments, cartilage, skin, and the dentin of teeth. The leather obtained from animal hides is actually tightly-packed collagen. If collagen is boiled, it dissolves and forms gelatin.   A.J.C./J.J.F.

Collenchyma is a stiff plant tissue. This magnified cross section of a leaf shows how collenchyma "fills out" much of the leaf.

COLLENCHYMA (kə leng′ kə mə) Collenchyma is the plant tissue that develops when the cells are filled with cellulose. These cells can lengthen to allow for growth of the plant. Collenchyma gives the plant strength and structure, and is usually found in stems and leaves. It is the major source of support for herbaceous plants. In woody plants, the collenchyma is crushed as the woody tissue begins to form. Collenchyma of the flax plant is used to make linen, a valuable type of cloth. *See also* FIBER.   A.J.C./E.R.L.

COLLOID (käl′ oid′) A colloid is made up of tiny particles of one substance dispersed

Below, colloidal particles are precipitated out of a solution (changed into solid particles that sink to the bottom of the flask).

(spread evenly) in another substance. The particles are large single molecules or large groups of smaller molecules. The particles are extremely small, ranging in diameter from about 3 millimicrons (1 millimicron = 1 billionth of a meter) to about 4,000 millimicrons. All living things contain colloids.

Colloids can be made up of any combination of solids, liquids, and gases except gases combined with gases. A suspension is a colloid of solid particles dispersed in a liquid. If the particles are dispersed in water, the colloid is called a sol or hydrosol. Many solid-liquid colloids look like jelly. They are called gels. A colloid of liquid particles or droplets dispersed in another liquid is an emulsion. A dispersion of gas in a liquid is a foam. A colloid of solid particles in a gas is a smoke. A colloid of a gas in a solid is a solid foam, such as foam rubber. Colloids of solid particles dispersed in solids can be made, such as ruby glass. Ruby glass consists of gold particles dispersed in glass.

Colloids can be made by grinding or churning materials together until the tiny colloidal particles form. Some colloids are made by chemical reactions. Colloids can also be made by striking an electric arc between materials in a liquid.

A colloid may look like a solution. However, a beam of light shone through the liquid shows up the particles. This effect, known as the Tyndall effect, is not seen in a solution. (*See* SOLUTION AND SOLUBILITY.)

Colloids can be broken down into three main groups, according to their chemical behavior. Lyophobic, or "solvent-hating," colloids are not very stable (able to stay dispersed). Some remain stable only because of electric charges on the particles. The particles repel one another, therefore remaining dispersed.

In lyophilic, or "solvent-loving," colloids, the colloids are more stable. Lyophilic colloids are found in animal and plant fluids.

The molecules of association colloids have a hydrocarbon chain. This chain has a hydrophilic (water-loving) "head" group with a hydrophobic (water-hating) "tail" group. Such molecules form clusters called micelles. The micelles keep the head groups in contact with water. They also protect the tails from water within the micelle. Detergents and soaps are common examples of association colloids.

Protoplasm and most other fluids in living things are colloids. Many products are colloids during manufacture, such as ceramics, cosmetics, foods, paints, papers, pesticides, and plastics. J.J.A./A.D.

Below, an example of the use of colloidal solutions in industry. A colloidal rubber solution, or latex, is poured into a mold. A foam rubber mattress is then made by closing the mold and hardening the latex. Colloids can be made of almost any combination of solids, liquids, and gases.

COLOBUS (kä′ lə bəs) The colobus monkey is a thumbless African monkey that lives in the tops of tall trees in tropical forests. It may grow as tall as 55 to 60 cm [22 to 24 in], and has a tail that may be 85 cm [34 in] long. The guereza or Abyssinian colobus monkey (*Colobus guereza*) is black with long, white fur around the face and on the tail. Colobus mon-

Facing left, the Abyssinian colobus monkey.

keys are plant-eaters and have a special stomach with several compartments, similar to that of ruminants.   A.J.C./J.J.M.

COLOR

Color (kəl' ər) is an aspect of light that allows humans and some animals to tell the difference between objects that are otherwise identical. The things we see all reflect certain wavelengths of light. (*See* LIGHT.) Eyes that have color vision contain structures which "see" different wavelengths of light as being different colors.

The light from the sun is commonly called "white" light. It is made up of all wavelengths or, as we know it, many colors put together. To show this, we can break white light down into its spectrum of various colors using a prism. These are the colors we see in rainbow. These same colors can be combined, using a second prism, back into white light.

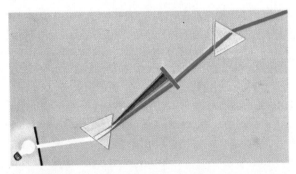

By the use of a color filter, a beam of light of a single color can be made from a beam of white light. A prism splits the white light into its spectrum of colors. A filter, placed in the spectrum beam, will absorb some colors. The colors which are passed, or transmitted, by the filter can be recombined by another prism to make a single beam of colored light.

When light reaches an object, some wavelengths are reflected (bounced back) and some are absorbed (taken in). The wavelengths that are reflected make up the color we see. If the skin of an apple reflects "red" wavelengths and absorbs all others, we see that skin as being red. A white object reflects practically all the light. A black object absorbs practically all the light.

Any two or more colors of light can be combined to form another color of light. All colors of light mixed together make white light. This method of mixing colors is called the additive method.

Red, green, and blue are commonly called the primary colors of light. Any two of these colors can easily be mixed to form a third color. All three can be mixed to form white light. To demonstrate additive color mixing, put a red slide, a green slide, and a blue slide in three separate slide projectors. Project the colors on a white surface and move them around so that the colors overlap slightly. When red and blue overlap, we get a color called magenta. When blue and green overlap, we see the color called cyan. When red and green overlap, we see yellow. Color television depends on the principle of additive color mixture.

When colors in pigments such as paints and dyes are mixed together, they combine differently from the colors of light. They do not combine by the additive method, but rather by the subtractive method. In the additive method, more light is reflected as more colors are mixed. In the subtractive method, more light is absorbed as more colors are mixed. When an artist uses pigments to paint a bowl of fruit, he or she is mixing the colors by the subtractive method. The artist can make any color needed using three primaries. With the subtractive method, the three common primaries are magenta, yellow, and cyan (blue green). For the painting, magenta and yellow could be mixed to paint an orange. Yellow and cyan could be mixed to get a green for grapes. For the black in the bowl, all three primary colors could be mixed together.

As with the additive method, many other colors can be made by mixing the primaries in different amounts.

Two or more colors are said to be complementary to each other when they mix to form white by the additive method or black by the subtractive method. Green and magenta are complementary colors of light. Yellow and blue are complementary colors of paint.

Several different systems of classifying colors have been worked out. Color experts can describe a color using three terms: hue, saturation, and brightness. Hue is the basic name for the color, like red or blue. Saturation is the amount of hue in the color. "Fire-engine red" is highly saturated, but pink is not. Lightness tells us how light or dark the color is. (*See* COLORIMETRY.)

Using these terms, colors can be arranged so that they can be accurately described. In the United States, the National Bureau of Standards and the Inter-Society Color Council have devised a system for naming colors. They have named and standardized 270 different colors. These standardized colors are used in the textile industry, in the making of cosmetics, and in the standardization of house paints.

In nature, color is important for certain creatures. It plays a role in the courtship behavior of many kinds of birds and fish. The coloration of certain young animals enables them to blend in with natural settings, thus becoming almost hidden from their enemies. A blossom of a plant may attract certain bees or butterflies that will land on it. Then they will carry pollen to another flower for pollination and fertilization.

Some people have defective vision that prevents them from seeing certain colors. (*See* COLOR BLINDNESS.) Some animals cannot see color at all. Dogs and cats, horses, pigs, and many other creatures live in a world of grays. *See also* EYE AND VISION.

P.G.C./S.S.B.

We see colors such as those in this scene because our eyes react to certain wavelengths of light. Our brains interpret these reactions as "color."

COLORADO POTATO BEETLE (käl′ ə rod′ ō pə tāt′ ō bēt′əl) The Colorado potato beetle (*Leptinotarsa decemlineata*) is a very destructive insect that attacks potato plants. This beetle is also called the potato bug. It is about 13 mm [0.5 in] long, with hard, yellow and black striped wing covers. The female lays clusters of eggs on potato leaves two or three times a year. These eggs produce pink larvae which feed on the leaves for about three weeks. They then drop to the ground, bury themselves, and spend the next ten days developing into adults. (*See* METAMORPHOSIS.)

Native to Mexico and the southwestern United States, the Colorado potato beetle had reached the Atlantic coast by 1875. Its natural enemies include snakes, birds, toads, and parasites. The pest is usually controlled by insecticides.

A.J.C./J.R.